# Contents

**Note for parents, tutors, teachers and other adult helpers**

A pull-out answers section (pages A1 to A12) appears in the centre of this book, between pages 26 and 27 (Paper 4). This provides correct answers to all the **English skills** and **Comprehension** questions, as well as guidelines for marking the **Short writing tasks**. It also gives simple guidance on how best to use this book. Remove the pull-out section before the child begins working through the practice papers.

You may wish the child to have access to a dictionary – either while he or she is working through the papers or after you have marked them. Make a decision on this before the child begins work. You may also give the child some separate sheets of lined paper for continuing the **Short writing task** if needed.

# English Progress Paper 1

START HERE

**Q. 1–60 English skills**                                                                                   MARK

| **Q. 1–5** punctuation | Rewrite the sentence correctly, adding the necessary punctuation. Put in capital letters, speech marks, commas, apostrophes and full stops. |
|---|---|

megan wont be at school in the morning because shell be going to the dentist mrs brown explained to the teacher

_____

_____

_____

_____ 1–5 ☐ 5

---

**Q. 6–10**
nouns

Add to the sentence a noun that is made from the word shown in capitals.

**6** HIGH  The balloon soared to a great _____.  6 ☐ 1

**7** RECEIVE  Make sure you get a _____ for your money.  7 ☐ 1

**8** MARRY  Their _____ will take place next year in May.  8 ☐ 1

**9** ABLE  I'm not sure I have the _____ to do this job.  9 ☐ 1

**10** STRONG  Lifting this box will take all my _____.  10 ☐ 1

---

**Q. 11–15**
word choice

Three words appear in brackets. Underline the *one* word that completes the sentence correctly.

**11** There is the boy (who, whose, whom) gave me the book.  11 ☐ 1

**12** (Who, Whom, Whose) have you come to see?  12 ☐ 1

**13** I have come to see (there, they're, their) father.  13 ☐ 1

**14** We (lied, layed, lay) down on the soft grass.  14 ☐ 1

**15** To become an expert you must (practice, practise) every day.  15 ☐ 1

MARK ☐

English skills                                                                    MARK

| Q. 16–20 | Underline the *one* word that is closest in meaning to the word shown in capitals. | |
|---|---|---|
| word meanings, synonyms | **16** CELEBRATED     green,    persevere,    clamour,    poor,    famous | 16 ☐ 1 |
| | **17** LETHAL     ugly,    dangerous,    delicious,    greedy,    tiny | 17 ☐ 1 |
| | **18** ACCURATE     fiddly,    kind,    healthy,    exact,    small | 18 ☐ 1 |
| | **19** DONATE     lose,    strive,    give,    secrete,    please | 19 ☐ 1 |
| | **20** LIVID     dead,    false,    innocent,    murky,    angry | 20 ☐ 1 |

| Q. 21–25 | Change the sentence from indirect (reported) speech to direct speech. For example, *Dr Jones suggested I rest my ankle till the swelling went down* becomes *"Do rest that ankle till the swelling goes down," suggested Dr Jones.* | |
|---|---|---|
| indirect to direct speech | **21** The teacher said I had to re-do my homework. _____ | 21 ☐ 1 |
| | **22** Mum asked why we were so late getting home. _____ | 22 ☐ 1 |
| | **23** George told Harry he was sorry for what he had done. _____ | 23 ☐ 1 |
| | **24** The student said he was sick of doing exams. _____ | 24 ☐ 1 |
| | **25** My gran told me my laces were undone – again! _____ | 25 ☐ 1 |

| Q. 26–30 | Change the singular word(s) to plural. If an apostrophe is used, make sure that you put it in the correct position. For example, *the lady's dog* becomes *the ladies' dogs.* | |
|---|---|---|
| apostrophes for possession, plurals | **26** the man's shoe    _____ | 26 ☐ 1 |
| | **27** my sister-in-law    _____ | 27 ☐ 1 |
| | **28** his mother's birthday    _____ | 28 ☐ 1 |
| | **29** man, woman and child    _____ | 29 ☐ 1 |
| | **30** the dictionary's definition    _____ | 30 ☐ 1 |

MARK ☐

English skills                                                                    MARK

| Q. 31–35 spelling | Write out the sentence, correcting any misspellings. | |
|---|---|---|

**31** It was the most intresting film we'd ever scene.

_____          31 ☐ 1

**32** You'll probaly miss youre train if you don't hurry.

_____          32 ☐ 1

**33** He'd groan so much I didn't reconise him.

_____          33 ☐ 1

**34** Sanjay apoligised so sincerly that he was let of.

_____          34 ☐ 1

**35** Did you recieve the present? I scent it first class.

_____          35 ☐ 1

| Q. 36–40 abbreviations | Write the words that the abbreviation (shortened form) stands for. | |
|---|---|---|

**36** EU          _____          36 ☐ 1

**37** www         _____          37 ☐ 1

**38** PS          _____          38 ☐ 1

**39** NB          _____          39 ☐ 1

**40** a.m. (as in 11.30 a.m.)   _____          40 ☐ 1

| Q. 41–45 alphabetical order | Put the words in alphabetical order by writing the numbers from 1 to 5 in the brackets. | |
|---|---|---|

**41** colour (___), cord (___), colt (___), corridor (___), cooler (___)          41 ☐ 1

**42** drip (___), dreary (___), dragon (___), drink (___), dragging (___)          42 ☐ 1

**43** felt (___), ferry (___), fence (___), feel (___), fetch (___)          43 ☐ 1

**44** psalm (___), pheasant (___), pseudo (___), philately (___), psychiatrist (___)          44 ☐ 1

**45** eyrie (___), eerie (___), eeriness (___), ear (___), eerily (___)          45 ☐ 1

MARK ☐

## English skills

MARK

| **Q. 46–50** | Write down the antonym (opposite) of the word. | | |
|---|---|---|---|
| antonyms | **46** temporary _____ | | **46** ☐ 1 |
| | **47** arrival _____ | | **47** ☐ 1 |
| | **48** transparent _____ | | **48** ☐ 1 |
| | **49** generous _____ | | **49** ☐ 1 |
| | **50** expand _____ | | **50** ☐ 1 |

**Q. 51–55**

comparative and superlative

Using the example as a guide, write the comparative and superlative of the adjective given. You may need to use more than one word.

| | ADJECTIVE | COMPARATIVE | SUPERLATIVE | |
|---|---|---|---|---|
| Example: | FINE | *finer* | *finest* | |
| **51** | WEAK | _____ | _____ | **51** ☐ 1 |
| **52** | HEALTHY | _____ | _____ | **52** ☐ 1 |
| **53** | HOPEFUL | _____ | _____ | **53** ☐ 1 |
| **54** | SMALL | _____ | _____ | **54** ☐ 1 |
| **55** | KINDLY | _____ | _____ | **55** ☐ 1 |

**Q. 56–60**

apostrophes for abbreviation

Abbreviate (shorten) the phrase by using an apostrophe.
For example, *They are not coming* becomes *They're not coming*.

| **56** one of the clock | _____ | **56** ☐ 1 |
|---|---|---|
| **57** he will not | _____ | **57** ☐ 1 |
| **58** they do not | _____ | **58** ☐ 1 |
| **59** Is she not going? | _____ | **59** ☐ 1 |
| **60** Where have you put my coat? | _____ | **60** ☐ 1 |

MARK ☐

ENGLISH SKILLS SUB-TOTAL ☐ 60

## Q. 61–75 Comprehension

MARK

Read this passage carefully.

# Fearsome Monster or Noble Beast?

*A brief introduction to the dragon as seen by different cultures.*

What do you think of when you picture a dragon? A fire-breathing, winged and tailed, scaly monster? A terrifying creature that imprisons princesses and guards great hoards of treasure? A noble and
5  fantastic beast with great strength? Or a hapless victim of a gallant knight who thrusts a spear down its throat?

You will doubtless have seen pictures of dragons and will know stories about their doings. All
10  countries and cultures have their own dragon myths and legends. Some see their beasts as snake-like. Others imagine them as marine creatures, emerging from the seas to terrify – or to save – as the mood takes them. In China, dragons are seen as powerful
15  and important. Dragons in the Slavic countries are many-headed and Turkish dragons breathe fire – not through their mouths but from their tails!

But the Welsh have a rather different view of their fabulous monster. They even have a bright
20  red dragon on their national flag. True, the Welsh red dragon is as fearsome as similar beasts found elsewhere – with its long forked tongue and fiery looks – but the Welsh people are very proud of their
25  dragon and he appears everywhere. You will find him on every local council's signs and headed paper, on documents, on sports' clubs badges, in arts centres, choirs' programmes and even on stamps!

Stories of the famous red Welsh dragon go far back
30  in history. In some myths he is seen as the symbol of the brave Welsh, whereas the invading Saxons are depicted as a white dragon. The story is linked to the father of the great King Arthur and his Knights of the Round Table. King Arthur's father was Uther
35  Pendragon – 'Pen' meaning 'head' or 'chief' – so his name meant, mysteriously, 'Uther Chief Dragon'! A famous early historian tells us that this was because Uther saw a dragon-shaped comet one night and, taking this as a good omen for the
40  coming battle, had one embroidered on his standard – the flag carried before his armies.

Now read these questions. You have a choice of four answers to each question. Choose the *one* answer you think the best. Draw a line in the box next to its letter, like this.

A ▭

**61** Which word best describes our views of dragons?

A various
B identical
C dangerous
D imaginary

A ▢
B ▢
C ▢
D ▢

61 ▢ 2

**62** From what source or sources do we learn about dragons?

A history
B art
C legends and myths
D television

A ▢
B ▢
C ▢
D ▢

62 ▢ 2

MARK ▭

## Comprehension

MARK

**63** Which word best describes the meaning of the word 'hapless' (line 5)?

   A  cheerful

   B  miserable

   C  unfortunate

   D  cowardly

63   2

**64** Which word is similar in meaning to 'legend' (line 11)?

   A  fable

   B  tradition

   C  picture

   D  history

64   2

**65** What is the meaning of 'marine' (line 12)?

   A  swimming

   B  amphibious

   C  evil

   D  living in the sea

65   2

**66** 'Fabulous' (line 19) comes from the noun 'fable'. What does this suggest about dragons?

   A  that they are not real

   B  that they are very exciting

   C  that they are popular

   D  that they are scary

66   2

**67** Which of the following statements is *not* true?

   A  Welsh dragons look intimidating.

   B  The red dragon is a popular symbol in Wales.

   C  The Welsh are ashamed of their dragon.

   D  It is not difficult to spot a red dragon in Wales.

67   2

**68** Who were the Saxons?

   A  people who wanted to take over Welsh territory

   B  white dragons

   C  mythical people who liked fighting

   D  people who hid inside a white dragon

68   2

MARK

## Comprehension

MARK

**69** Why did Uther have a dragon on his standard?

A because he thought it would frighten the enemy    A ☐

B because he wanted a dragon-shaped comet    B ☐

C because he was going into battle    C ☐

D because he thought it was a lucky sign    D ☐    **69** ☐ 2

**70** Which of the phrases below would best complete the sentence?

The writer finds stories of dragons _____.

A frightening and dangerous    A ☐

B fascinating and colourful    B ☐

C random and weird    C ☐

D complicated and old-fashioned    D ☐    **70** ☐ 2

**71** Some people may view the dragon as a 'terrifying creature that imprisons princesses and guards great hoards of treasure' (lines 3–4).
Which of the following words is used in the extract as a verb?

A terrifying    A ☐

B hoards    B ☐

C creature    C ☐

D guards    D ☐    **71** ☐ 2

Find the spelling mistake. Underline it and write the box letter at the end of the line.

**72**

| Dragonology | is the official | sceintific name | for dragon studies. | |
|---|---|---|---|---|
| A | B | C | D | ☐ |

    **72** ☐ 2

**73**

| There are numerous | mysterious | mythalogical | creatures. | |
|---|---|---|---|---|
| A | B | C | D | ☐ |

    **73** ☐ 2

**74**

| The people of | Whales regard | the dragon as their | national mascot. | |
|---|---|---|---|---|
| A | B | C | D | ☐ |

    **74** ☐ 2

**75**

| Dragons probably | never actually | existed exept | in our imagination. | |
|---|---|---|---|---|
| A | B | C | D | ☐ |

    **75** ☐ 2

MARK ☐

COMPREHENSION SUB-TOTAL ☐ 30

## Q. 76–85 Short writing task

MARK

Write for 15–30 minutes on *one* of the following. Continue on a separate sheet if you need to.

a) You have discovered a baby dragon. Describe it in detail.

b) Treasure!

c) Do you enjoy myths and legends? How important do you think they are?

_____

_____

_____

_____

_____

_____

_____

_____

_____

_____

_____

_____

_____

_____

_____

_____

_____

_____

_____

_____

_____

END OF TEST

| SHORT WRITING TASK SUB-TOTAL | | 10 |
|---|---|---|
| English skills sub-total (from page 5) | | 60 |
| Comprehension sub-total (from page 8) | | 30 |
| Short writing task sub-total (from this page) | | 10 |
| PROGRESS PAPER 1 TOTAL MARK | | 100 |

# English Progress Paper 2

START HERE

## Q. 1–60 English skills

MARK

| Q. 1–5 punctuation | Rewrite the sentence correctly, adding the necessary punctuation. | |
|---|---|---|
| | im very sorry dr kumar isnt here at the moment said the receptionist but hell be back soon | 1–5 ☐ 5 |

| Q. 6–10 nouns | Add to the sentence a noun that is made from the word shown in capitals. | |
|---|---|---|
| | **6** GRAND  They were awestruck by the _____ of the view. | 6 ☐ 1 |
| | **7** SUCCEED  Sandip enjoyed his _____ in the contest. | 7 ☐ 1 |
| | **8** CURIOUS  The proverb says that _____ killed the cat. | 8 ☐ 1 |
| | **9** LAZY  Ava's constant _____ lost her the job. | 9 ☐ 1 |
| | **10** MUSICAL  The _____ played the piece well. | 10 ☐ 1 |

| Q. 11–15 homonyms | Write the *one* word that has *both* meanings. | |
|---|---|---|
| | In one of these items, the word is pronounced differently depending on the meaning. | |
| | **11** small new plant / to fire a gun _____ | 11 ☐ 1 |
| | **12** unit of time / very tiny indeed _____ | 12 ☐ 1 |
| | **13** quick lowering of the head / aquatic bird _____ | 13 ☐ 1 |
| | **14** short period of time / magic formula _____ | 14 ☐ 1 |
| | **15** strong- and spicy-tasting root / reddish orange colour _____ | 15 ☐ 1 |

MARK ☐

English skills                                                                 MARK

| | |
|---|---|
| **Q. 16–20**<br><br>word choice | Two words appear in brackets. Underline the *one* word that completes the sentence correctly.<br><br>**16** The speaker talked about (current, currant) affairs.<br><br>**17** He (swim, swam, swum) across the river.<br><br>**18** The (principal, principle) addressed the school.<br><br>**19** None of us (are, is, am) going out today.<br><br>**20** Can you (prophecy, prophesy) what will happen? |

16 ☐ 1

17 ☐ 1

18 ☐ 1

19 ☐ 1

20 ☐ 1

| | |
|---|---|
| **Q. 21–25**<br><br>parts of speech, nouns, adjectives, adverbs, verbs | Read the sentence. Decide whether the underlined word is a noun, an adjective, an adverb or a verb. Write your answer on the line.<br><br>**21** I haven't packed much – my backpack is <u>light</u>. _____<br><br>**22** I can't talk now so I'll call you <u>later</u>. _____<br><br>**23** Please finish your <u>practice</u> before the film starts. _____<br><br>**24** I asked her the time but she couldn't <u>advise</u> me. _____<br><br>**25** My cat's <u>favourite</u> toy is his squeaky mouse. _____ |

21 ☐ 1

22 ☐ 1

23 ☐ 1

24 ☐ 1

25 ☐ 1

| | |
|---|---|
| **Q. 26–30**<br><br>comparative and superlative | Using the example as a guide, write the comparative and superlative of the adjective given. You may need to use more than one word. |

|  | ADJECTIVE | COMPARATIVE | SUPERLATIVE | |
|---|---|---|---|---|
| Example: | ROUGH | *rougher* | *roughest* | |
| **26** | LITTLE | _____ | _____ | 26 ☐ 1 |
| **27** | BAD | _____ | _____ | 27 ☐ 1 |
| **28** | THOUGHTFUL | _____ | _____ | 28 ☐ 1 |
| **29** | TINY | _____ | _____ | 29 ☐ 1 |
| **30** | THIN | _____ | _____ | 30 ☐ 1 |

MARK ☐

English skills

MARK

**Q. 31–35**

past tense

Add to the sentence the past tense of the verb shown in capitals.

**31** CREEP I have _____ into the cellar.

31 ☐ 1

**32** EAT I have _____ your dinner.

32 ☐ 1

**33** SING I have _____ in the concert.

33 ☐ 1

**34** FIGHT I have _____ against the bullies.

34 ☐ 1

**35** SPEAK I have _____ up for her.

35 ☐ 1

**Q. 36–40**

grammar, spelling

Write out the sentence, correcting any errors.

**36** This is the best of the two games.

_____

36 ☐ 1

**37** Each of the girls had their doll.

_____

37 ☐ 1

**38** We new she had broke her leg.

_____

38 ☐ 1

**39** We couldn't answer none of the questions.

_____

39 ☐ 1

**40** Neither of them were hurt in the accident.

_____

40 ☐ 1

**Q. 41–45**

direct to indirect speech

Change the sentence from direct to indirect (reported) speech.

**41** "Where have you been?" Mum asked Kassim.

_____

41 ☐ 1

**42** "I don't feel very well," said Tom.

_____

42 ☐ 1

**43** "It's time I went to school," replied Zofia.

_____

43 ☐ 1

**44** "How far is it to Leeds?" Sam asked the attendant.

_____

44 ☐ 1

**45** "It's only about 10 miles," he replied.

_____

45 ☐ 1

MARK ☐

English skills

MARK

| | | |
|---|---|---|
| **Q. 46–50**<br>spelling | Read the clue. Fill in the missing letters to make the word. | |
| | **46** somewhere to live      a __ __ __ __ m __ __ __ __ __ __ n | 46 ☐ 1 |
| | **47** to own      p __ __ __ __ __ __ | 47 ☐ 1 |
| | **48** a happening      o __ __ __ r __ __ __ __ __ | 48 ☐ 1 |
| | **49** to make someone blush      e __ __ __ __ __ __ __ | 49 ☐ 1 |
| | **50** at once      i __ __ __ __ __ __ __ __ y | 50 ☐ 1 |

| | | |
|---|---|---|
| **Q. 51–55**<br>adverbs,<br>suffixes | Add *ly* to the adjective to turn it into an adverb, making any changes needed as you do so. | |
| | **51** happy   _____ | 51 ☐ 1 |
| | **52** helpful   _____ | 52 ☐ 1 |
| | **53** casual   _____ | 53 ☐ 1 |
| | **54** wise   _____ | 54 ☐ 1 |
| | **55** fine   _____ | 55 ☐ 1 |

| | | |
|---|---|---|
| **Q. 56–60**<br>apostrophes<br>for<br>abbreviation | Abbreviate (shorten) the phrase by using an apostrophe.<br>For example, *Will she not do it?* becomes *Won't she do it?* | |
| | **56** You will eat later.   _____ | 56 ☐ 1 |
| | **57** Who has gone out?   _____ | 57 ☐ 1 |
| | **58** I have had enough.   _____ | 58 ☐ 1 |
| | **59** We cannot find it.   _____ | 59 ☐ 1 |
| | **60** All is well that ends well.   _____ | 60 ☐ 1 |

MARK ☐

ENGLISH SKILLS SUB-TOTAL ☐ 60

## Q. 61–75 Comprehension

Read this passage carefully.

### My Big Day

*Ahmad does his best to measure up.*

There were about 15 kids there when we arrived. I had been panicking about being late on this Big Day but the bus, which seemed to have yawned along the way and snoozed at every stop, woke up and almost galloped for the last half mile. Dad and I jumped off and ran to 171 High Street. I had expected a glossy studio but the door was ancient and peeling, the hallway was dark and smelled of old dinners and
5 the room into which we all crowded was dim and didn't have enough chairs. The girl who let us in wore weird black eye make-up and heels as high as a crane. She said her name was something that sounded like Mush. Some of the kids looked really nervous. One or two were practising their audition pieces, oblivious to everyone else in the room. Most of them were in jeans and hoodies, but a few dressed seriously cool as if they spent their lives on film sets and lunching with stars. I felt a bit embarrassed
10 about my trainers.

Mush called us away, one by one, to be auditioned. I breathed deeply and slowly as I had learned to do – ever since my first part in the school play, when I nearly died of nerves. It helped. I repeated my speech to myself with all the pauses and emphases in the right places. It was good. I knew I was good. I really wanted this part. I wanted to pay Dad back for all the work he'd done for me – getting me drama
15 lessons, taking a day off work to take me to the audition, persuading school to let me go. I wanted to make him proud of me. And I knew I could do it.

Suddenly – there it was – my name! I followed Mush down a corridor into a large room with three men and a woman sitting behind a long table. The woman looked up and said hello. Then the middle man looked up and frowned. He stared hard at me.
20 "How tall are you?" he asked.

"I'm 1.6 metres," I said, trembling slightly.

The man looked at the woman and I thought I saw him shake his head.

"I'm so sorry," she said. "That's just a bit too tall for this part. They should have told you."

Now read these questions. You have a choice of four answers to each question. Choose the *one* answer you think the best. Draw a line in the box next to its letter, like this.

A � box

**61** What does this passage describe?

   **A** taking part in a journey

   **B** taking part in a film

   **C** taking part in an audition

   **D** taking part in a fashion show

61 ☐ 2

**62** How is the bus described?

   **A** as if it were old and broken down

   **B** as if it were a sleepy animal

   **C** as being late and slow

   **D** as being very excitable

62 ☐ 2

MARK ☐

## Comprehension

MARK

**63** Which of the following phrases best describes 171 High Street?

    A smart and modern

    B crowded and unfriendly

    C noisy and brightly-lit

    D dilapidated and musty

63   2

**64** Which of these is another word for 'audition'?

    A rehearsal

    B speech

    C try-out

    D exam

64   2

**65** We are told that Mush wears 'heels as high as a crane' (line 6).
Of what kind of writing is this an example?

    A exaggeration

    B metaphor

    C measurement

    D simile

65   2

**66** Some of the girls and boys were 'oblivious to everyone else in the room' (line 8).
What does this mean?

    A They were trying to impress the others.

    B They were taking no notice of the others.

    C They were noisier than the others.

    D They were cleverer than the others.

66   2

**67** How does Ahmad, the narrator, feel by the end of the second paragraph?

    A unprepared and frightened

    B nervous and worried

    C excited and proud

    D calm and confident

67   2

**68** Which of the words below would best complete the sentence?

    Ahmad feels a great deal of _____ to his father.

    A gratitude

    B concern

    C hopefulness

    D generosity

68   2

MARK

## Comprehension

MARK

**69** The narrator has experienced several emotions during this extract. Which *two* of the following do you think might best describe his feelings by the end of the passage?

    1. nervousness  2. disappointment  3. anger  4. disapproval

A  2 and 3 only
B  1 and 4 only
C  2 and 4 only
D  1 and 3 only

A ☐
B ☐
C ☐
D ☐

**69** ☐ 2

**70** Think about how Ahmad might have felt after the audition. Which of the phrases below would best complete the sentence?

    The boy in the story felt _____ on account of his height.

A  not selected
B  discriminated against
C  impolitely ignored
D  disallowed

A ☐
B ☐
C ☐
D ☐

**70** ☐ 2

**71** Which of the following best describes the words 'High Street' (line 3) and 'Mush' (line 7).

A  common nouns
B  adjectives
C  verbs
D  proper nouns

A ☐
B ☐
C ☐
D ☐

**71** ☐ 2

Find the spelling mistake. Underline it and write the box letter at the end of the line.

**72**  There are usally   far more people   auditioning than there   are parts available.

    A         B         C         D     ☐

**72** ☐ 2

**73**  Children in films   have tutorial   arrangments so their   education continues.

    A         B         C         D     ☐

**73** ☐ 2

**74**  Filming can be   boring as hours   are waisted   awaiting your scene.

    A         B         C         D     ☐

**74** ☐ 2

**75**  The movie industry   is less glamorous   than it apears   in magazines.

    A         B         C         D     ☐

**75** ☐ 2

MARK ☐

COMPREHENSION SUB-TOTAL ☐ 30

## Q. 76–85 Short writing task

MARK

Write for 15–30 minutes on *one* of the following. Continue on a separate sheet if you need to.

a) Continue the story 'My Big Day' from where it leaves off (page 14).

b) Imagine you are Mush. Tell the story from your point of view.

c) Think of a room you know well. Describe it in detail so that a reader can picture it clearly.

_____

_____

_____

_____

_____

_____

_____

_____

_____

_____

_____

_____

_____

_____

_____

_____

_____

_____

_____

_____

_____

_____

END OF TEST

SHORT WRITING TASK SUB-TOTAL ☐ 10

English skills sub-total (from page 13) ☐ 60

Comprehension sub-total (from page 16) ☐ 30

Short writing task sub-total (from this page) ☐ 10

**PROGRESS PAPER 2 TOTAL MARK** ☐ 100

START HERE

## Q. 1–60 English skills

MARK

| Q. 1–5 | Rewrite the text correctly, adding the necessary punctuation. | |
|---|---|---|
| punctuation | excuse me shouted asha can you help me im stuck up this tree and i cant get down | |

1–5 ☐ 5

| Q. 6–10 | Add to the sentence a noun that is made from the word shown in capitals. | |
|---|---|---|
| nouns | | |

**6** DECIDE  It was a very tricky _____ to make.

6 ☐ 1

**7** PUNCTUAL  Never late, he was well-known for his _____.

7 ☐ 1

**8** FAMOUS  Mum's _____ spread when her new DVD came out.

8 ☐ 1

**9** REVEAL  The newspaper's _____ shocked us all.

9 ☐ 1

**10** SPEAK  I believe in the freedom of _____ for all.

10 ☐ 1

| Q. 11–15 | Three words appear in brackets. Underline the *one* word that completes the sentence correctly. |
|---|---|
| word choice | |

**11** A meteorite probably (destructed, destroyed, distracted) the dinosaurs.

11 ☐ 1

**12** People who have seizures may suffer from (epilepsy, episodes, epicentre).

12 ☐ 1

**13** The house was designed by a famous (archaeologist, artefact, architect).

13 ☐ 1

**14** At university you can study many (disciplines, disciples, discussions).

14 ☐ 1

**15** A naturalist studies the (habitats, inhabits, habitual) of different creatures.

15 ☐ 1

MARK ☐

English skills                                                                    MARK

---

**Q. 16–20**

similes

Put the word in the simile to which it belongs.

houses, lamb, rock, rake, doornail

**16** as dead as a _____                    16 ☐ 1

**17** as thin as a _____                    17 ☐ 1

**18** as steady as a _____                   18 ☐ 1

**19** as safe as _____                      19 ☐ 1

**20** as meek as a _____                    20 ☐ 1

---

**Q. 21–25**

parts of speech, verbs, adverbs

Read the sentence. Write V under the verb(s), P under the pronoun(s) and ADV under the adverb(s).

**21** She pushed vigorously.

                                                                21 ☐ 1

**22** They came here.

                                                                22 ☐ 1

**23** We met before.

                                                                23 ☐ 1

**24** He howled interminably.

                                                                24 ☐ 1

**25** She ran doggedly round the track.

                                                                25 ☐ 1

---

**Q. 26–30**

abbreviations

Write the words that the abbreviation (shortened form) stands for.

**26** NSPCC _____                    26 ☐ 1

**27** UK _____                       27 ☐ 1

**28** RAC _____                      28 ☐ 1

**29** PO _____                       29 ☐ 1

**30** MA _____                       30 ☐ 1

---

MARK ☐

English skills                                                                                    MARK

| Q. 31–35 antonyms | Write down the antonym (opposite) of the word. | |
|---|---|---|

**31** professional _____     31 ☐ 1

**32** senior _____     32 ☐ 1

**33** elder _____     33 ☐ 1

**34** winning _____     34 ☐ 1

**35** remote _____     35 ☐ 1

---

**Q. 36–40**
word groups
(by meaning)

Underline the *one* word that may be used to describe all the others.

**36** speak, communicate, write, telephone, text     36 ☐ 1

**37** alder, cedar, birch, tree, beech     37 ☐ 1

**38** fly, travel, sail, walk, ride     38 ☐ 1

**39** spaniel, terrier, dog, Labrador, collie     39 ☐ 1

**40** flu, measles, mumps, illness, chickenpox     40 ☐ 1

---

**Q. 41–45**
apostrophes
for
possession

Abbreviate (shorten) the phrase by using an apostrophe.
For example, *the bone belonging to the dog* becomes *the dog's bone.*

**41** the wings belonging to the fly _____     41 ☐ 1

**42** the uniform of the police officer _____     42 ☐ 1

**43** the house belonging to Mr Thomas _____     43 ☐ 1

**44** the tail of the lioness _____     44 ☐ 1

**45** the squeaks of the mice _____     45 ☐ 1

MARK ☐

## English skills

MARK

### Q. 46–50
homonyms

Write the *one* word that has *both* meanings.

**46** to get off (a bus, for example) / on fire _____    46 ☐ 1

**47** form of transport with carriages / to teach someone a skill _____    47 ☐ 1

**48** a postal label on a letter / to push down sharply with one's foot

_____    48 ☐ 1

**49** a herb / wise or a wise person _____    49 ☐ 1

**50** to take something that is someone else's / to creep around quietly

_____    50 ☐ 1

### Q. 51–55
odd one out
(by meaning)

Underline the *one* word that is the odd one out.

**51** colleague, accomplice, helper, enemy, ally    51 ☐ 1

**52** plumber, driver, bricklayer, electrician, plasterer    52 ☐ 1

**53** lazy, mad, crazy, loony, nuts    53 ☐ 1

**54** crab, plaice, halibut, bream, sardine    54 ☐ 1

**55** academy, school, college, university, classroom    55 ☐ 1

### Q. 56–60
spelling

Read the clue. Fill in the missing letters to make the word.

**56** worried    a __ __ __ __ __ __    56 ☐ 1

**57** the opposite of ugly    b __ __ __ __ __ __ __ __    57 ☐ 1

**58** the flat surface above and facing the floor    c __ __ __ __ __ __    58 ☐ 1

**59** required, essential    n __ __ __ __ __ a __ __    59 ☐ 1

**60** a senior teacher at a university    p __ __ f __ __ __ __ __    60 ☐ 1

MARK ☐

ENGLISH SKILLS SUB-TOTAL ☐ 60

## Q. 61–75 Comprehension

Read this passage carefully.

# YOU CAN'T KEEP A GOOD MAN DOWN!

*Stonecaster's mountain-climbing grandfather is off again.*

A Stonecaster man is about to embark on a challenge. Pawel Robinski, 69, is packing his rucksack and ready to take on Mount Everest. He's no beginner, though he admits that Everest is quite daunting. He's a veteran of Kilimanjaro, 5 the highest mountain in Africa, followed by Aconcagua, the highest in the Americas, and Cho Oyu, another Himalayan monster. "I've been busy getting fit," says grandfather of three, Pawel. "Sean, the landlord of my local pub, The Three Pigeons, must wonder what's become of me as 10 I've been keeping off the beer. They see a lot more of me at the gym than the pub these days." However, he plans to pop into his local soon. "I hope they'll all sponsor me. All the regulars know me, so I'm sure they will."

However, preparations for the trip are hard work 15 and Pawel is looking forward to coming home again. "I'll be glad when it's done," he admits. "It's going to be an amazing adventure but all this abstinence is tough. I will be keen to get back to my real life – down The Pigeons and in my favourite Indian restaurant, the Koh-i-Noor on

20 Castle Street. I'll be pretty scrawny by the time I get back – and ready to put on a few pounds again!"

Pawel will raise money for the local hospice, Rosemead Priory. "Rosemead was great with my mum some years back, so I want to help them now that I can," says Pawel. 25 Elspeth Martin, Lead Consultant at Rosemead, says, "We're thrilled by Pawel's undertaking and we wish him all the best. Everyone at Rosemead is amazingly dedicated and selfless in their care for our residents and it is immensely rewarding when someone helps us in 30 this way in return."

Pawel plans to write a daily blog about his climb. "I want people back home – especially family and friends who sponsor me – to get a real feel for what it's like. I just hope my hands are not too cold to type!"

35 *If you would like to sponsor Pawel, visit www.pawelforeverest.com – where you can also see pictures of Pawel and his preparations for the trip.*

Now read these questions. You have a choice of four answers to each question. Choose the *one* answer you think the best. Draw a line in the box next to its letter, like this.

**61** The title of this article is 'You Can't Keep a Good Man Down!' In the context of the article as a whole, which word best describes this title?

   A joke
   B pun
   C teaser
   D heading

**61** ☐ 2

**62** Pawel is ready '<u>to take on</u> Mount Everest' (lines 2–3). What does the underlined phrase suggest about the peak?

   A It is a very high mountain.
   B It is a formidable enemy.
   C It is waiting for Pawel.
   D It is cold and dangerous.

**62** ☐ 2

MARK ☐

## Comprehension

MARK

**63** Cho Oyu is described as 'another Himalayan monster' (lines 6–7). Which of the following phrases is closest to conveying this description of Cho Oyu?

A huge and dangerous
B savage and fierce
C ugly and predatory
D high up and frightening

A ☐
B ☐
C ☐
D ☐

63 ☐ 2

**64** Who are 'the regulars' (line 13)?

A the people in the gym that Pawel uses
B the other mountain climbers
C the people that Pawel sees each day
D the people who often visit The Three Pigeons

A ☐
B ☐
C ☐
D ☐

64 ☐ 2

**65** What is an experienced mountain climber known as?

A a mountainer
B a mounter
C a mountainous
D a mountaineer

A ☐
B ☐
C ☐
D ☐

65 ☐ 2

**66** Pawel says that 'all this abstinence is tough' (line 17). What is 'abstinence'?

A giving up things you enjoy
B hard exercise and fitness training
C not drinking beer
D not eating Indian food

A ☐
B ☐
C ☐
D ☐

66 ☐ 2

**67** Abstinence is a noun. Which *one* of the following is the related verb?

A abstine
B abstain
C abstone
D abstinate

A ☐
B ☐
C ☐
D ☐

67 ☐ 2

**68** What is a 'hospice' (line 22)?

A a café where all are welcome
B an old people's home
C a nursing home that cares for people at the end of their lives
D a shop that sells things for charity

A ☐
B ☐
C ☐
D ☐

68 ☐ 2

MARK ☐

## Comprehension

MARK

**69** What is the meaning of 'dedicated and selfless' (line 28)?

A committed to working hard for others

B uncaring and selfish

C well-educated and energetic

D intelligent and careful

A ☐
B ☐
C ☐
D ☐          69 ☐ 2

**70** How does Pawel hope to share his adventure with others?

A by sending home photographs and getting people to sponsor him

B by drinking beer with his friends and writing a blog every day

C by sending home photographs and writing a blog every day

D by getting people to sponsor him and writing a blog every day

A ☐
B ☐
C ☐
D ☐          70 ☐ 2

**71** Which of the following phrases describes Pawel *least* accurately?

A adventurous and fit

B energetic and unselfish

C idle and uncaring

D brave and fearless

A ☐
B ☐
C ☐
D ☐          71 ☐ 2

Find the grammatical mistake. Underline it and write the box letter at the end of the line.

**72**  Pawel, who's       very fit, is       considerably braver    than you or I.

| A | B | C | D |
|---|---|---|---|

☐          72 ☐ 2

**73**  The mountain what   Pawel will climb   is apparently the   highest in the world.

| A | B | C | D |
|---|---|---|---|

☐          73 ☐ 2

**74**  Me and my friend    raised money by    running 5 km    for the Hospice.

| A | B | C | D |
|---|---|---|---|

☐          74 ☐ 2

**75**  We made more    for good causes    than we'd ever of    done otherwise.

| A | B | C | D |
|---|---|---|---|

☐          75 ☐ 2

MARK ☐

COMPREHENSION SUB-TOTAL ☐ 30

## Q. 76–85 Short writing task

MARK

Write for 15–30 minutes on *one* of the following. Continue on a separate sheet if you need to.

a) The Challenge

b) Write Pawel's blog the evening after he has spent a particularly difficult day on Everest.

c) You have never before seen snow and arrive for the first time in this country when everything is white. Write a letter home describing what you are experiencing.

END OF TEST

| | |
|---|---|
| SHORT WRITING TASK SUB-TOTAL | 10 |
| English skills sub-total (from page 21) | 60 |
| Comprehension sub-total (from page 24) | 30 |
| Short writing task sub-total (from this page) | 10 |
| PROGRESS PAPER 3 TOTAL MARK | 100 |

# English Progress Paper 4

START HERE

## Q. 1–60 English skills

MARK

| | | |
|---|---|---|
| **Q. 1–5**<br>punctuation | Rewrite the text correctly, adding the necessary punctuation.<br><br>   help yelled the zoo keeper cuthbert the lion has escaped<br><br>_____<br><br>_____<br><br>_____ | 1–5 ☐ 5 |

| | | |
|---|---|---|
| **Q. 6–10**<br>spelling | Write out the text, correcting any misspellings. | |
| | **6** I can't wait untill you get home – I must leave immediatly.<br><br>_____<br>_____ | 6 ☐ 1 |
| | **7** Have you a peice of paper on which to wright your adress?<br><br>_____<br>_____ | 7 ☐ 1 |
| | **8** "Wait a minuit," he yelled. "I am buying some jiuce!"<br><br>_____<br>_____ | 8 ☐ 1 |
| | **9** Unusally, he didn't rember the begining of the poem.<br><br>_____<br>_____ | 9 ☐ 1 |
| | **10** I'm completly exorsted and I need a choclate biscit!<br><br>_____<br>_____ | 10 ☐ 1 |

| | | | |
|---|---|---|---|
| **Q. 11–15**<br>antonyms | Write down the antonym (opposite) of the word. | | |
| | **11** scarce | _____ | 11 ☐ 1 |
| | **12** innocent | _____ | 12 ☐ 1 |
| | **13** exit | _____ | 13 ☐ 1 |
| | **14** easy | _____ | 14 ☐ 1 |
| | **15** neat | _____ | 15 ☐ 1 |

MARK ☐

# Progress Papers
# Answers

## English **1**

Schofield&Sims

# Progress Papers in English 1

## Notes for parents, tutors, teachers and other helpers

This pull-out book contains correct answers to all the questions in **Progress Papers in English 1**, and is designed to assist you, the adult helper, as you mark the child's work. Once the child has become accustomed to the method of working, you may wish to give him or her direct access to this pull-out section.

When marking, write the number of marks achieved in the tinted column on the far right of the question page. **The number to the right of the white mark box indicates the maximum mark available for that question.** Sub-total boxes at the foot of each page will help you to add marks quickly. You can then fill in the total marks at the end of the paper. Here you can record separately the child's score in each of the three parts of the paper. The total score is out of 100 and therefore yields a percentage result. To keep track of the child's progress, use the **Progress chart** on page 52.

Each paper is divided into three sections, as follows.

**Progress Papers in English 1 – structure of each paper, with key facts for adult helpers**

|  | Number of questions | Total marks available | Approximate time available |
|---|---|---|---|
| **English skills** | 60 | 60 | 15–20 minutes |
| **Comprehension** | 15 | 30 | 20–30 minutes |
| **Short writing task** | The child chooses and completes one of three tasks, for which 10 marks may be gained. | 10 | 15–30 minutes |
| **Totals** | **85 questions** | **100 marks** | **50–80 minutes** |

## English skills (60 questions, worth a total of 60 marks)

This first section comprises 12 groups of five brief questions. In **Progress Papers in English 1**, you can expect children to take **between 15 and 20 minutes** to complete it. Each group of questions tests a particular area of literacy skill or knowledge. Most of the questions in this first section have right or wrong answers (for example, the plural of *man* is *men*). However, some do not and a range of answers is possible. If the question asks, for example, for a sentence to be changed from indirect to direct speech then some variation from the suggested answer is acceptable. You must make your own judgement concerning these questions.

The questions in this section are worth one mark if answered correctly. The only exception is the somewhat longer punctuation question at the start of each paper, which is allocated a maximum of five marks. In all questions like these, where the right answer includes several different elements, give full marks only if the response is completely correct and covers all the constituent parts.

Some English words can be spelt correctly in more than one way. For a free download providing notes and guidance on alternative spellings, visit any of the **Progress Papers in English** pages on the Schofield & Sims website (www.schofieldandsims.co.uk).

## Comprehension (15 questions, worth a total of 30 marks)

The second section offers passages for comprehension followed by 15 multiple-choice questions, each with a choice of four possible answers – only one of which should be chosen. The Comprehension section in this book should take children **between 20 and 30 minutes** to answer. The questions vary in difficulty, but you should tell the child to assume that they are more difficult than they might at first appear. Encourage the child to read carefully both the passage and the question before answering. Sometimes, the distinction between several of the possible answers offered is subtle: care and re-reading of both the passage and the question may be needed before the choice is made.

A correctly answered Comprehension question is worth two marks. This reflects the importance of these questions, which test understanding of the passage as well as grammar and spelling.

# Short writing task (worth a total of 10 marks)

The third section allows the child **between 15 and 30 minutes** to write a brief composition on one of three topics. Space is available for the piece of writing to be written on the page, directly below the list of topics. However, the child may need an extra sheet of paper on which to continue, so be sure to have some available.

Marking a child's composition is not an exact science, but generally speaking you should give credit for strengths and deduct marks for deficiencies. The guidelines below will help you to give the child's writing a mark out of 10. **Please bear in mind that, at this level, it should not be impossible for a lively and accurately written piece to gain full marks.**

Where an essay title is provided, this may be interpreted exactly as the child wishes. For example, the title 'Treasure!' (Paper 1, option b) could prompt the child to write a fictional story or a newspaper report. In total, this series provides 54 essay topics, requiring a range of writing skills and styles as listed opposite, used for a variety of purposes and aimed at different readers. Help the child to understand that not all writing is the same: they would not write a thank-you letter to their grandparents in the same style as a speech to be read out in class or a story for a younger child.

The table opposite highlights different aspects of style – arranged by task type and designed to help you as you mark different types of writing. Discourage the child from always choosing the 'story' option. The experience of tackling the varied writing tasks provided in this series will give the child the skills and confidence to write well – not just in English tests but in all other aspects of study and life where writing matters.

### Short writing task – general marking guidelines

| Give credit for: | Deduct marks for: |
|---|---|
| • writing in a style appropriate to the task and audience (see table opposite) | • inappropriate style – for example, too formal or informal for purpose and/or audience (see table opposite) |
| • correct spelling and punctuation, legible handwriting | • poor spelling and/or illegibility |
| • appropriate use of paragraphing and the setting out of dialogue | • inadequate or misplaced punctuation, paragraphing, use of capital letters |
| • correct grammar (allow some leeway for, for example, colloquial conversation, especially if it is expressive of individual character) | • writing that loses its way, is irrelevant to the title, doesn't make sense or is repetitive |
| • consistency within the piece of writing in the use of verb tenses | • inconsistent use of verb tenses – moving from past to present or vice versa |
| • use of interesting, varied and lively vocabulary | • inconsistent narrative approach – for example, changing from third person to first person or changing tenses mid-narrative |
| • narrative, descriptive or explicatory flair – for example, in holding the reader's attention, story twists, imaginative use of language | • a sense that the writer is not in control and is either struggling to write enough or struggling to contain an idea that is too big for the time allowed |
| • an overall sense of control and confidence | |

## Short writing task – marking for style

| Task type | Book 1 | |
|---|---|---|
| **Story writing**<br>• A 30-minute time limit does not allow for a large cast or for several changes of place and day. The story will work best if the action happens all in one go, in one location and with only a few participants.<br>• It is best for the child to avoid a long introduction, unless it is vital to the story. Award an extra mark if the child plunges straight into the story. This is particularly important, of course, if the child has been asked to continue the story where it left off or to write from a particular character's viewpoint.<br>• Even bearing in mind these limitations, you may still find pace, dialogue and description that helps you to imagine the events, setting and atmosphere. | Paper 1b)<br>Paper 2a)<br>Paper 2b)<br>Paper 3a) | Paper 4a)<br>Paper 5a)<br>Paper 6a)<br>Paper 6b) |
| **Concise description**<br>• Look for evidence that the child has taken account of the intended audience for the piece of writing and adjusted his or her style accordingly.<br>• For example, if the piece of writing requested is for a website or magazine, look for a concise style that will keep the attention of readers: watch out for too much detail, particularly any facts that are irrelevant to the audience. | Paper 1b)<br>Paper 3b) | Paper 5a)<br>Paper 5c) |
| **Detailed description**<br>• Where a full description is required, give marks for clearly imagined and carefully crafted prose.<br>• Look for descriptions that give a strong sense of the person, place or thing. | Paper 1a)<br>Paper 1b)<br>Paper 2a)<br>Paper 2c)<br>Paper 3a)<br>Paper 3c) | Paper 4a)<br>Paper 4c)<br>Paper 5b)<br>Paper 6b) |
| **Instructions, persuasive writing and explanations**<br>• Clarity of thinking makes for clarity of expression. Before the child starts writing, he or she needs first to identify the purpose of the piece of writing.<br>• *Instructions* need to be simple, correctly ordered and straightforward.<br>• *Writing that aims to persuade or to influence* should avoid nagging or insulting the reader. Carefully worked-out arguments – clearly expressed and with separate points that are logically ordered – can be very effective.<br>• *Explanation* must be clearly focused on exactly what it is that the reader needs to understand. Always look for evidence that the child understands what he or she is trying to explain. You cannot provide a clear explanation of something that you do not understand. | | Paper 4b)<br>Paper 5c) |
| **Discussion**<br>• As above, look for clarity of thinking and expression, as well as evidence that the child has some understanding of the issue under discussion.<br>• Strong opinions are not needed: being able to see several sides to a question is a valuable skill.<br>• Simple sentences may work best in writing of this kind. | Paper 1c) | Paper 6c) |
| **Conversation and dialogue**<br>• Some questions invite the child to write a conversation, develop or create one or more characters, or speak in the voice of a particular character. Since we do not all speak in the same way, written conversation should convey a sense of the speaker, the context and the subject matter.<br>• All conversation should be correctly set out and punctuated. | Paper 2b)<br>Paper 3b) | Paper 5b) |

## Progress Paper 1
## English skills

**1–5** "Megan won't be at school in the morning because she'll be going to the dentist," Mrs Brown explained to the teacher.

| | |
|---|---|
| 6 | height |
| 7 | receipt |
| 8 | marriage |
| 9 | ability |
| 10 | strength |
| 11 | who |
| 12 | Whom |
| 13 | their |
| 14 | lay |
| 15 | practise |
| 16 | famous |
| 17 | dangerous |
| 18 | exact |
| 19 | give |
| 20 | angry |

There are several possible answers to questions 21–25. Those given are examples only.

**21** "You have to re-do your homework," said the teacher. *or* "This homework has to be re-done," said the teacher. *or* "You must re-do your homework," said the teacher.

**22** "Why are you so late getting home?" asked Mum. *or* "Why were you so late getting home?" asked Mum. *or* "What made you so late in getting home?" asked Mum.

**23** "Harry, I'm really sorry about what I did," said George. *or* "Harry, I'm really sorry about what I have done," said George.

## Paper 1 – *continued*

**24** "I am sick of exams!" said the student. *or* "I am sick of taking exams!" said the student.

**25** "Your laces are undone – again!" said my gran.

| | |
|---|---|
| 26 | the men's shoes |
| 27 | our sisters-in-law |
| 28 | their mothers' birthdays |
| 29 | men, women and children |
| 30 | the dictionaries' definitions |

**31** It was the most <u>interesting</u> film we'd ever <u>seen</u>.

**32** You'll <u>probably</u> miss <u>your</u> train if you don't hurry.

**33** He'd <u>grown</u> so much I didn't <u>recognise</u> him.

**34** Sanjay <u>apologised</u> so <u>sincerely</u> that he was let <u>off</u>.

**35** Did you <u>receive</u> the present? I <u>sent</u> it first class.

| | |
|---|---|
| 36 | European Union |
| 37 | world wide web |
| 38 | post scriptum *or* postscript |
| 39 | nota bene *(meaning 'note well')* |
| 40 | ante meridian |
| 41 | colour (1), colt (2), cooler (3), cord (4), corridor (5) |
| 42 | dragging (1), dragon (2), dreary (3), drink (4), drip (5) |
| 43 | feel (1), felt (2), fence (3), ferry (4), fetch (5) |
| 44 | pheasant (1), philately (2), psalm (3), pseudo (4), psychiatrist (5) |
| 45 | ear (1), eerie (2), eerily (3), eeriness (4), eyrie (5) |
| 46 | permanent |
| 47 | departure |
| 48 | opaque |
| 49 | mean *or* miserly |
| 50 | contract *or* shrink |

## Paper 1 – *continued*

| | |
|---|---|
| 51 | weaker, weakest |
| 52 | healthier, healthiest |
| 53 | more hopeful, most hopeful |
| 54 | smaller, smallest |
| 55 | kindlier/more kindly, kindliest/most kindly |
| 56 | one o'clock |
| 57 | he won't *or* he'll not |
| 58 | they don't |
| 59 | Isn't she going? |
| 60 | Where've you put my coat? |

## Comprehension

| | |
|---|---|
| 61 | A |
| 62 | C |
| 63 | C |
| 64 | A |
| 65 | D |
| 66 | A |
| 67 | C |
| 68 | A |
| 69 | D |
| 70 | B |
| 71 | D |
| 72 | C sceintific *(should be 'scientific')* |
| 73 | C mythalogical *(should be 'mythological')* |
| 74 | B Whales *(should be 'Wales')* |
| 75 | C exept *(should be 'except')* |

## Short writing task

Refer to general guidelines on page A4 and specific notes on page A5 as indicated.

| | |
|---|---|
| a) | Detailed description |
| b) | Story writing, Concise description, Detailed description |
| c) | Discussion |

## Progress Paper 2
## English skills

1–5 | "I'm very sorry, Dr Kumar isn't here at the moment," said the receptionist, "but he'll be back soon."
*A comma or a dash may be used after the word 'sorry'.*

6 | grandeur
7 | success
8 | curiosity
9 | laziness
10 | musician

11 | shoot
12 | minute
13 | duck
14 | spell
15 | ginger

16 | current
17 | swam
18 | principal
19 | is ('are' *would be an acceptable alternative in informal writing or in speech*)
20 | prophesy

21 | adjective
22 | adverb
23 | noun
24 | verb
25 | adjective

26 | littler, littlest
27 | worse, worst
28 | more thoughtful, most thoughtful
29 | tinier, tiniest
30 | thinner, thinnest

31 | crept
32 | eaten
33 | sung
34 | fought
35 | spoken

## Paper 2 – *continued*

36 | This is the <u>better</u> of the two games.
37 | Each of the girls had <u>her</u> doll.
38 | We <u>knew</u> she had <u>broken</u> her leg.
39 | We couldn't answer <u>any</u> of the questions. *or* We <u>could</u> answer none of the questions.
40 | Neither of them <u>was</u> hurt in the accident.
*(In informal writing or in speech, 'Neither of them were hurt in the accident' would be acceptable.)*

41 | Mum asked Kassim where he had been.
42 | Tom said that he didn't feel very well.
43 | Zofia replied that it was time she went to school.
44 | Sam asked the attendant how far it was (*or* is) to Leeds. *or* Sam asked the attendant the distance to Leeds.
45 | He replied that it was (*or* is) only about 10 miles.

46 | accommodation
47 | possess
48 | occurrence
49 | embarrass
50 | immediately

51 | happily
52 | helpfully
53 | casually
54 | wisely
55 | finely

56 | You'll eat later.
57 | Who's gone out?
58 | I've had enough.
59 | We can't find it.
60 | All's well that ends well.

## Paper 2 – *continued*
## Comprehension

61 | C
62 | B
63 | D
64 | C
65 | A
66 | B
67 | D
68 | A
69 | A
70 | B
71 | D
72 | A usally (*should be* 'usually')
73 | C arrangments (*should be* 'arrangements')
74 | C waisted (*should be* 'wasted')
75 | C apears (*should be* 'appears')

## Short writing task

Refer to general guidelines on page A4 and specific notes on page A5 as indicated.

a) | Story writing, Detailed description
b) | Story writing, Conversation and dialogue
c) | Detailed description

## Progress Paper 3
## English skills

**1–5** "Excuse me!" shouted Asha. "Can you help me? I'm stuck up this tree and I can't get down!"
*A full stop could be used instead of the second exclamation mark – either would be correct.*

**6** decision
**7** punctuality
**8** fame
**9** revelation
**10** speech

**11** destroyed
**12** epilepsy
**13** architect
**14** disciplines
**15** habitats

**16** doornail
**17** rake
**18** rock
**19** houses
**20** lamb

**21** She (P) pushed (V) vigorously (ADV).
**22** They (P) came (V) here (ADV).
**23** We (P) met (V) before (ADV).
**24** He (P) howled (V) interminably (ADV).
**25** She (P) ran (V) doggedly (ADV) round the track.

**26** National Society for the Prevention of Cruelty to Children
**27** United Kingdom
**28** Royal Automobile Club
**29** Post Office
**30** Master of Arts

## Paper 3 – *continued*

**31** amateur *or* lay *or* unprofessional
**32** junior
**33** younger
**34** losing
**35** close *or* near *or* central
*Other possible antonyms include 'likely' or 'strong' (of a possibility) and 'friendly' or 'approachable' (of a person).*

**36** communicate
**37** tree
**38** travel
**39** dog
**40** illness

**41** the fly's wings
**42** the police officer's uniform
**43** Mr Thomas'(s) house
**44** the lioness's tail
**45** the mice's squeaks

**46** alight
**47** train
**48** stamp
**49** sage
**50** steal

**51** enemy
**52** driver
**53** lazy
**54** crab
**55** classroom

**56** anxious
**57** beautiful
**58** ceiling
**59** necessary
**60** professor

## Paper 3 – *continued*
## Comprehension

**61** B
**62** B
**63** A
**64** D
**65** D
**66** A
**67** B
**68** C
**69** A
**70** D
**71** C
**72** D than you or I (should be 'me')
**73** A The mountain what (should be 'that')
**74** A Me and my friend (should be 'My friend and I')
**75** C than we'd ever of (should be 'have')

## Short writing task

Refer to general guidelines on page A4 and specific notes on page A5 as indicated.

**a)** Story writing, Detailed description
**b)** Concise description, Conversation and dialogue
**c)** Detailed description

## Progress Paper 4
## English skills

1–5 | "Help!" yelled the zoo keeper. "Cuthbert the lion has escaped!" *or* "Help!" yelled the zoo keeper, Cuthbert. "The lion has escaped!"

6 | I can't wait until you get home – I must leave immediately.

7 | Have you a piece of paper on which to write your address?

8 | "Wait a minute!" he yelled. "I am buying some juice!"

9 | Unusually, he didn't remember the beginning of the poem.

10 | I'm completely exhausted and I need a chocolate biscuit!

11 | plentiful *or* abundant *or* common

12 | guilty

13 | entrance *or* enter

14 | difficult *or* hard

15 | untidy *or* messy

16 | He and I were playing outdoors.

17 | The car passed me at great speed.

18 | He has led me up the garden path.

19 | Can I borrow your pen for a while?

20 | He gave it to Louis and me.

21 | type

22 | stand

23 | junk

24 | fawn

25 | spoke

## Paper 4 – *continued*

26 | lemonade

27 | football

28 | sandals

29 | mansion

30 | plumber

31 | chosen

32 | drunk

33 | torn

34 | ridden

35 | laid

36 | United Nations

37 | post meridian

38 | miles per hour

39 | millimetre(s)

40 | Her/His Royal Highness

41 | I took the purse I had found to the police station. *or* I found a purse, which I took to the police station.

42 | I went to see my gran, who lives in Hull.

43 | He completed the walk, which was tiring.

44 | She was late for school as (*or* because) she had got up late.

45 | Bob catches the number 4 bus as (*or* because) it stops by his home. *or* Bob catches the number 4 bus, which stops by his home.

46 | cheap/cheep

47 | muscle/mussel

48 | raw/roar

49 | pause/paws

50 | loan/lone

51 | unique

52 | infrequent

53 | official

54 | complement

55 | rare

## Paper 4 – *continued*

56 | Liam's mum ate her son's (*or* sons') breakfast.

57 | The boys did hours of work at their stepdad's farm.

58 | The doctor's (*or* doctors') assistant came to the children's ward.

59 | Mohammed's brother picked up the lady's cat.

60 | The ladies' and gentlemen's toilets are at the back.

## Comprehension

61 | C

62 | D

63 | A

64 | C

65 | A

66 | B

67 | B

68 | B

69 | D

70 | C

71 | D

72 | C puncuality (*should be 'punctuality'*)

73 | C especialy (*should be 'especially'*)

74 | B particulary (*should be 'particularly'*)

75 | D tunnells (*should be 'tunnels'*)

## Short writing task

Refer to general guidelines on page A4 and specific notes on page A5 as indicated.

a) | Story writing, Detailed description

b) | Instructions, persuasive writing and explanations

c) | Detailed description

## Progress Paper 5
### English skills

| | |
|---|---|
| 1–5 | "Ow!" cried Annie's baby's nanny. "I think I've broken my ankle!" |
| 6 | depth |
| 7 | open |
| 8 | unfriendly *or* hostile |
| 9 | free *or* release |
| 10 | include |
| 11 | the butterfly's wings |
| 12 | the butterflies' wings |
| 13 | James'(s) football |
| 14 | three weeks' wages |
| 15 | half an hour's work |
| 16 | shoot (1), shore (2), short (3), shot (4), shrimp (5) |
| 17 | addict (1), ado (2), adore (3), adventure (4), advertise (5) |
| 18 | quarter (1), queasy (2), queueing (3), quirky (4), quite (5) |
| 19 | trip (1), tripe (2), triple (3), triplet (4), triplicate (5) |
| 20 | pool (1), pouch (2), poulterer (3), poultice (4), poultry (5) |
| 21 | luckier, luckiest |
| 22 | funnier, funniest |
| 23 | tastier, tastiest |
| 24 | heavier, heaviest |
| 25 | easier, easiest |
| 26 | length |
| 27 | width |
| 28 | height |
| 29 | depths |
| 30 | breadth |

## Paper 5 – *continued*

| | |
|---|---|
| 31 | The contented cat (N) purred (V) as he lay (V) on the rug (N). |
| 32 | Enraged, Jacob (N) fought (V) off the attacker (N). |
| 33 | Mum (N) screamed (V) as the heavy book (N) fell (V) on her foot (N). |
| 34 | "Sit!"(V) shouted (V) Harry (N) to the excitable dog (N). |
| 35 | The fast hare (N) overtook (V) the slow tortoise (N). |
| 36 | want not |
| 37 | catches the worm |
| 38 | run deep |
| 39 | soonest mended |
| 40 | the sun shines |
| 41 | bank |
| 42 | room |
| 43 | tank |
| 44 | start |
| 45 | frank |
| 46 | justify |
| 47 | shelve |
| 48 | clothe |
| 49 | struck |
| 50 | horrified |
| 51 | mistook |
| 52 | misled |
| 53 | mislaid |
| 54 | misunderstood |
| 55 | miscast |
| 56 | cauliflower |
| 57 | elephant |
| 58 | pigeon |
| 59 | juggernaut |
| 60 | apostrophe |

## Paper 5 – *continued*

### Comprehension

| | |
|---|---|
| 61 | A |
| 62 | B |
| 63 | B |
| 64 | D |
| 65 | C |
| 66 | C |
| 67 | B |
| 68 | D |
| 69 | B |
| 70 | A |
| 71 | A |
| 72 | D felicities *(should be 'facilities')* |
| 73 | B conversationalists *(should be 'conservationists')* |
| 74 | B successively *(should be 'successfully')* |
| 75 | B respect *(should be 'aspect')* |

### Short writing task

Refer to general guidelines on page A4 and specific notes on page A5 as indicated.

| | |
|---|---|
| a) | Story writing, Concise description |
| b) | Detailed description, Conversation and dialogue |
| c) | Instructions, persuasive writing and explanations, Concise description |

## Progress Paper 6
## English skills

**1–5** "My favourite book,"
said Lily, "is 'Horrid Henry'
by Francesca Simon."
*Ensure that the child uses
capital letters for
Horrid Henry, but omitting
inverted commas around
the title should not be
treated as an error at this
stage.*

**6** The Captain ordered
William to prepare
to cast off.

**7** Meena asked me whether
I was (*or* am) going to
take the test.

**8** The plasterer told Dad to
be careful as the floor was
(*or* is) unsafe.

**9** As Sam slunk in, the
teacher told him that
he was late again.

**10** Oli asked if he might have
some more as he was still
hungry. *or* As Oli was still
hungry, he asked if he
might have some more.

**11** counterfeit
**12** sovereign
**13** perceive
**14** niece
**15** weir

**16** She didn't speak
very <u>clearly</u>.
**17** The teacher <u>taught</u>
him many facts. *or* The
teacher learned many
facts. (*Omit 'him'.*)
**18** <u>She</u> and <u>I</u> went shopping.
**19** He was so helpful,
I could <u>have</u> hugged him.
**20** Priya <u>laid</u> the table
before the meal.

## Paper 6 – *continued*

**21** eel
**22** die
**23** sheet
**24** mustard
**25** feather

**26** inveigle
**27** seize
**28** heifer
**29** receipt
**30** sieve

**31** lazy, lazily
**32** thoughtful, thoughtfully
**33** deep, deeply
**34** high, highly
**35** strong, strongly

**36** Great Britain
**37** kilometre(s)
**38** United States of America
**39** application (software)
**40** Member of Parliament

**41** I was so <u>surprised</u> at my
<u>success</u> in the race.
**42** I was <u>jealous</u> when he
was made <u>chief</u> monitor.
**43** I would <u>definitely</u> like
to meet the <u>author</u>.
**44** The <u>builder</u> was
<u>embarrassed</u> when
the <u>ceiling</u> fell in.
**45** I will start my own
<u>business</u> if I get
the <u>opportunity</u>.

**46** with a spine
**47** awkward and difficult
to handle
**48** with both hands
**49** survivor
**50** eats meat

**51** of
**52** at *or* against
**53** by
**54** to
**55** on

## Paper 6 – *continued*

**56** Spotting the burglar,
Yossi raced after him.
**57** Having picked up the
bone, the dog (then)
buried it.
**58** Whistling my favourite
song, I began vacuuming.
**59** Finishing the race,
he collapsed as he
crossed the line.
**60** Hanging on to the
mugger, Chloë shouted
for help. *or* Shouting for
help, Chloë hung on to
the mugger.

## Comprehension

**61** D
**62** B
**63** B
**64** A
**65** B
**66** D
**67** B
**68** C
**69** B
**70** C
**71** A
**72** A likly (*should be 'likely'*)
**73** D descision (*should be
'decision'*)
**74** D payed (*should be 'paid'*)
**75** A actualy (*should be
'actually'*)

## Short writing task

Refer to general guidelines
on page A4 and specific notes
on page A5 as indicated.

**a)** Story writing
**b)** Story writing,
Detailed description
**c)** Discussion

This book of answers is a pull-out section from
**Progress Papers in English 1**

First published in 1993
Revised edition published in 2015
Copyright © Schofield & Sims Ltd 2015

Authors: Patrick Berry and Susan Hamlyn

Patrick Berry and Susan Hamlyn have asserted their moral right under the Copyright, Designs and Patents Act, 1988, to be identified as the authors of this work.

Design by **Ledgard Jepson Ltd**

Printed in the UK by **Wyndeham Gait Ltd**, Grimsby, Lincolnshire

ISBN 978 07217 1310 6

**British Library Catalogue in Publication Data:**
A catalogue record for this book is available from the British Library.

## English skills

MARK

**Q. 16–20**

grammar, spelling

Write out the sentence, correcting any errors.

**16** Him and me was playing outdoors.

_____

16 ☐ 1

**17** The car past me at great speed.

_____

17 ☐ 1

**18** He has lead me up the garden path.

_____

18 ☐ 1

**19** Can I lend your pen for a while?

_____

19 ☐ 1

**20** He gave it to Louis and I.

_____

20 ☐ 1

---

**Q. 21–25**

homonyms

Write the *one* word that has *both* meanings.

**21** a kind / used in printing _____

21 ☐ 1

**22** a frame for displaying things / to be upright _____

22 ☐ 1

**23** rubbish / a Chinese boat _____

23 ☐ 1

**24** a young deer / to flatter in a slimy way _____

24 ☐ 1

**25** talked / part of a bicycle wheel _____

25 ☐ 1

---

**Q. 26–30**

anagrams

Unscramble the anagram to fit the meaning given.
For example, *GENORA (a fruit)* is an *ORANGE*.

**26** DELONAME (a drink) _____

26 ☐ 1

**27** BOLTFOAL (a sport) _____

27 ☐ 1

**28** DANLASS (footwear) _____

28 ☐ 1

**29** NNMSAIO (a large house) _____

29 ☐ 1

**30** BLUEPRM (someone who fixes leaks and drains) _____

30 ☐ 1

MARK ☐

English skills

MARK

---

**Q. 31–35**

past tense

Add to the sentence the past tense of the verb shown in capitals.

**31** CHOOSE  I have _____ my new shoes.

**32** DRINK  I have _____ too much.

**33** TEAR  I have _____ my shirt.

**34** RIDE  I have _____ Noah's bike.

**35** LAY  He has _____ the table.

| 31 | | 1 |
| 32 | | 1 |
| 33 | | 1 |
| 34 | | 1 |
| 35 | | 1 |

---

**Q. 36–40**

abbreviations

Write the words that the abbreviation (shortened form) stands for.

**36** UN  _____

**37** p.m. (as in 2.30 p.m.)  _____

**38** mph  _____

**39** mm  _____

**40** HRH  _____

| 36 | | 1 |
| 37 | | 1 |
| 38 | | 1 |
| 39 | | 1 |
| 40 | | 1 |

---

**Q. 41–45**

join sentences

Join the two sentences *without* using *and, but* or *so*.
For example, *The boy washed my car. I thanked the boy* becomes
*I thanked the boy who washed my car* or *I thanked the boy for washing my car.*

**41** I found a purse. I took the purse to the police station.

_____

**42** I went to see my gran. My gran lives in Hull.

_____

**43** He completed the walk. The walk was tiring.

_____

**44** She was late for school. She had got up late.

_____

**45** Bob catches the number 4 bus. It stops by his home.

_____

_____

| 41 | | 1 |
| 42 | | 1 |
| 43 | | 1 |
| 44 | | 1 |
| 45 | | 1 |

MARK _____

English skills

MARK

---

**Q. 46–50**

homophones

Read the clues, then write the homophones (words that sound the same).
For example, *water from above* is *rain* / *what the monarch does* is *reign*.

**46** inexpensive _____ / a chirp made by a young bird _____

46 ☐ 1

**47** part of the body that helps us move _____ / a shellfish _____

47 ☐ 1

**48** uncooked _____ / a lion does it _____

48 ☐ 1

**49** a short break _____ / animal feet _____

49 ☐ 1

**50** borrowed money _____ / solitary _____

50 ☐ 1

---

**Q. 51–55**

word choice

Put the word in the sentence where it makes the best sense.

official, complement, unique, rare, infrequent

**51** This vase is _____, being the only one of its kind.

51 ☐ 1

**52** The village receives only an _____ bus service.

52 ☐ 1

**53** It's an _____ sign so we'd better not trespass.

53 ☐ 1

**54** The mustard was the perfect _____ to the steak.

54 ☐ 1

**55** The eggs of _____ birds are protected by law.

55 ☐ 1

---

**Q. 56–60**

apostrophes
for
possession

Rewrite the sentence, adding apostrophe(s) as you do so.

**56** Liams mum ate her sons breakfast.

_____

56 ☐ 1

**57** The boys did hours of work at their stepdads farm.

_____

57 ☐ 1

**58** The doctors assistant came to the childrens ward.

_____

58 ☐ 1

**59** Mohammeds brother picked up the ladys cat.

_____

59 ☐ 1

**60** The ladies and gentlemens toilets are at the back.

_____

60 ☐ 1

---

MARK ☐

ENGLISH SKILLS SUB-TOTAL ☐ 60

## Q. 61–75 Comprehension

Read this passage carefully.

### No Time to Lose

*Cassie is worried about her grandfather.*

The inhaler was lying there on the table. Cassie froze.

"Oh no!" she breathed. "Not again!"

She looked at the little green clock on the cooker. 12.17. The train was due to leave at 12.34 and he'd been gone around four minutes. Could she – if she ran like a racehorse – get to the station before he got
5 on the train? She grabbed her jacket, her keys and her purse. The laces of her trainers were undone and her fingers struggled to tie them, too fast to be accurate. She tore open the front door and slammed it behind her, already half way down the path as it banged shut.

Her brain raced. Which was the quickest way? Was it best to guess which route he'd have taken and try to head him off? Was it better to just get to the station the fastest possible way and hope to be there
10 when he arrived? But there were two entrances to the station. He might take either. What should she do?

She pictured him, as she pelted through the shopping centre, sitting on the train, the train slipping away from the platform and then, suddenly, his breath going, his throat constricting, his face turning beige as the air wouldn't come, choking, collapsing . . . He'd fumble for the inhaler – the other passengers wouldn't understand, they'd think he was drunk, they'd ignore him – and the inhaler wouldn't be
15 in his pocket.

A woman was setting out a table in front of her café. Two men came out, laughing. There was no space between them and the table. Cassie couldn't avoid them. She hurtled into them, sending one staggering into the wall.

"Sorry!" she tried to call out as she shot between them, but she had no breath left to make a sound.
20 The shopping centre clock clanged 12.30 and she still hadn't seen her grandfather.

Now read these questions. You have a choice of four answers
to each question. Choose the *one* answer you think the best.
Draw a line in the box next to its letter, like this.

A ▭

**61** What illness might someone who uses an inhaler (line 1) suffer from?

   A eczema

   B catarrh

   C asthma

   D arthritis

61 ☐ 2

**62** How long did Grandfather have between his leaving the house and the departure of the train?

   A 19 minutes

   B 27 minutes

   C 13 minutes

   D 21 minutes

62 ☐ 2

MARK ☐

## Comprehension

MARK

**63** 'if she ran like a racehorse' (line 4) is an example of a literary device. What is it called?

- A a simile
- B a personification
- C an exaggeration
- D an adjective

A ☐
B ☐
C ☐
D ☐

63 ☐ 2

**64** Which of the words below would best complete the sentence?

Cassie evidently feels a great sense of _____ towards her grandfather.

- A antipathy
- B impatience
- C responsibility
- D pity

A ☐
B ☐
C ☐
D ☐

64 ☐ 2

**65** Which of the following proverbs is suggested by Cassie's problems with her laces?

- A More haste, less speed.
- B Look before you leap.
- C Many hands make light work.
- D A miss is as good as a mile.

A ☐
B ☐
C ☐
D ☐

65 ☐ 2

**66** 'She tore open the front door and slammed it behind her, already half way down the path as it banged shut' (lines 6–7). How many verbs are there in this sentence?

- A four
- B three
- C one
- D two

A ☐
B ☐
C ☐
D ☐

66 ☐ 2

**67** Cassie is uncertain about what to do (lines 8–10). Which of the following words best sums up her state of mind in these lines?

- A confusion
- B dilemma
- C panic
- D hysteria

A ☐
B ☐
C ☐
D ☐

67 ☐ 2

**68** Cassie imagines her grandfather having an attack (lines 11–15). Which *one* of the following is *not* worrying her?

- A he will become seriously ill on the train
- B he won't have enough money
- C he has left his inhaler at home
- D the other passengers won't understand what is wrong with him

A ☐
B ☐
C ☐
D ☐

68 ☐ 2

MARK ☐

## Comprehension

MARK

**69** Cassie 'hurtled' into the men (line 17). Which of the following words is similar in meaning to 'hurtled'?

A  fell
B  smacked
C  sped
D  careered

A ☐
B ☐
C ☐
D ☐

69 ☐ 2

**70** Later in the story, Cassie reaches her grandfather just in time. If you were he, which *two* of the following words would describe your feelings?

1. grateful  2. apologetic  3. unconcerned  4. irritated

A  3 and 4 only
B  2 and 3 only
C  1 and 2 only
D  1 and 3 only

A ☐
B ☐
C ☐
D ☐

70 ☐ 2

**71** Which of the following is the best alternative title for this passage?

A  Station Drama
B  Granddad Forgets
C  Old and Young
D  Race Against Time

A ☐
B ☐
C ☐
D ☐

71 ☐ 2

Find the spelling mistake. Underline it and write the box letter at the end of the line.

**72**  Passengers are   more irritated by   lack of puncuality   than by dirty carriages.

A          B          C          D

☐   72 ☐ 2

**73**  Asthma is an   unpleasant condition,   especialy for children   and the elderly.

A          B          C          D

☐   73 ☐ 2

**74**  Many children   have particulary   affectionate relationships   with grandparents.

A          B          C          D

☐   74 ☐ 2

**75**  Sensations of   claustrophobia may   occur when travelling   through tunnells.

A          B          C          D

☐   75 ☐ 2

MARK ☐

COMPREHENSION SUB-TOTAL ☐ 30

## Q. 76–85 Short writing task

MARK

Write for 15–30 minutes on *one* of the following. Continue on a separate sheet if you need to.

a) Continue the story 'No Time to Lose' from where it leaves off (page 30).

b) Think of a gadget, game or tool you know well. Write careful instructions for its use.

c) Think of an elderly person you know well. Describe them, conveying an impression of their appearance and personality.

_____

_____

_____

_____

_____

_____

_____

_____

_____

_____

_____

_____

_____

_____

_____

_____

_____

_____

_____

_____

_____

_____

END OF TEST

| | |
|---|---|
| SHORT WRITING TASK SUB-TOTAL | 10 |
| English skills sub-total (from page 29) | 60 |
| Comprehension sub-total (from page 32) | 30 |
| Short writing task sub-total (from this page) | 10 |
| PROGRESS PAPER 4 TOTAL MARK | 100 |

START HERE

## Q. 1–60 English skills

MARK

| Q. 1–5 | Rewrite the text correctly, adding the necessary punctuation. | |
|---|---|---|
| punctuation | ow cried annies babys nanny i think ive broken my ankle | |

1–5 ☐ 5

| Q. 6–10 | Write down the antonym (opposite) of the word. | |
|---|---|---|
| antonyms | **6** height _____ | 6 ☐ 1 |
| | **7** closed _____ | 7 ☐ 1 |
| | **8** friendly _____ | 8 ☐ 1 |
| | **9** imprison _____ | 9 ☐ 1 |
| | **10** exclude _____ | 10 ☐ 1 |

| Q. 11–15 | Rewrite the phrase, adding an apostrophe as you do so. | |
|---|---|---|
| apostrophes for possession | **11** the butterflys wings _____ | 11 ☐ 1 |
| | **12** the butterflies wings _____ | 12 ☐ 1 |
| | **13** James football _____ | 13 ☐ 1 |
| | **14** three weeks wages _____ | 14 ☐ 1 |
| | **15** half an hours work _____ | 15 ☐ 1 |

MARK ☐

English skills                                                                                          MARK

| | | |
|---|---|---|

**Q. 16–20**

alphabetical order

Put the words in alphabetical order by writing the numbers from 1 to 5 in the brackets.

**16** shoot (___), short (___), shore (___), shot (___), shrimp (___)                16 ☐ 1

**17** adventure (___), advertise (___), adore (___), addict (___), ado (___)        17 ☐ 1

**18** queueing (___), quirky (___), queasy (___), quarter (___), quite (___)        18 ☐ 1

**19** triplet (___), triple (___), triplicate (___), trip (___), tripe (___)        19 ☐ 1

**20** poultry (___), pouch (___), poulterer (___), poultice (___), pool (___)       20 ☐ 1

**Q. 21–25**

comparative and superlative

Using the example as a guide, write the comparative and superlative of the adjective given.

| | ADJECTIVE | COMPARATIVE | SUPERLATIVE | |
|---|---|---|---|---|
| Example: | DIRTY | *dirtier* | *dirtiest* | |
| **21** | LUCKY | _____ | _____ | 21 ☐ 1 |
| **22** | FUNNY | _____ | _____ | 22 ☐ 1 |
| **23** | TASTY | _____ | _____ | 23 ☐ 1 |
| **24** | HEAVY | _____ | _____ | 24 ☐ 1 |
| **25** | EASY | _____ | _____ | 25 ☐ 1 |

**Q. 26–30**

nouns

Add to the sentence a noun that is made from the word shown in capitals.

**26** LONG  The swimming pool's _____ is enough for Olympic training.   26 ☐ 1

**27** WIDE  Can you work out the _____ of the garden?                  27 ☐ 1

**28** HIGH  The _____ of some city buildings is breathtaking!          28 ☐ 1

**29** DEEP  Some creatures live at enormous _____ at the bottom of the ocean.   29 ☐ 1

**30** BROAD  I measured the _____ of the canvas to make my tent.       30 ☐ 1

MARK ☐

## English skills

MARK

---

**Q. 31–35**

parts of
speech,
nouns,
verbs

Read the sentence. Write N under the noun(s) and V under the verb(s).

**31** The contented cat purred as he lay on the rug.

31 ☐ 1

**32** Enraged, Jacob fought off the attacker.

32 ☐ 1

**33** Mum screamed as the heavy book fell on her foot.

33 ☐ 1

**34** "Sit!" shouted Harry to the excitable dog.

34 ☐ 1

**35** The fast hare overtook the slow tortoise.

35 ☐ 1

---

**Q. 36–40**

proverbs
and sayings

Complete the proverb or saying.

**36** Waste not, _____ .

36 ☐ 1

**37** The early bird _____ .

37 ☐ 1

**38** Still waters _____ .

38 ☐ 1

**39** Least said, _____ .

39 ☐ 1

**40** Make hay while _____ .

40 ☐ 1

---

**Q. 41–45**

homonyms

Write the *one* word that has *both* meanings.

**41** at the edge of a river / place to keep money _____

41 ☐ 1

**42** space / one of several within a house or flat _____

42 ☐ 1

**43** place for fuel in a car / armoured vehicle _____

43 ☐ 1

**44** to begin / to jump with surprise _____

44 ☐ 1

**45** outspoken, honest / to stamp with an official mark _____

45 ☐ 1

---

MARK ☐

English skills

MARK

---

**Q. 46–50**

verbs

Add to the sentence a verb that is made from the word shown in capitals.

**46** JUST  I hope he can _____ what he has done.

46 ☐ 1

**47** SHELF  We must _____ our plans until later.

47 ☐ 1

**48** CLOTH  I need money to feed and _____ the baby.

48 ☐ 1

**49** STRIKE  We _____ up an agreement.

49 ☐ 1

**50** HORROR  He _____ me by telling me the cost.

50 ☐ 1

---

**Q. 51–55**

past tense

Add to the sentence the past tense of the verb shown in capitals.

**51** MISTAKE  He _____ me for someone else.

51 ☐ 1

**52** MISLEAD  When he told me the way he _____ me.

52 ☐ 1

**53** MISLAY  She has _____ her racquet and cannot play.

53 ☐ 1

**54** MISUNDERSTAND  The child had _____ all we'd said.

54 ☐ 1

**55** MISCAST  The actor playing The Doctor was _____ in that role.

55 ☐ 1

---

**Q. 56–60**

anagrams

Unscramble the anagram to fit the meaning given.
For example, *A DIRTY COIN (a book for checking spelling)* is a *DICTIONARY*.

**56** COW I ARE FULL (a vegetable) _____

56 ☐ 1

**57** NEAT HELP (an animal) _____

57 ☐ 1

**58** ONE PIG (a bird) _____

58 ☐ 1

**59** RUN JUG GATE (a large vehicle) _____

59 ☐ 1

**60** PAT SHE POOR (a punctuation mark) _____

60 ☐ 1

---

MARK ☐

ENGLISH SKILLS SUB-TOTAL ☐ 60

## Q. 61–75 Comprehension

MARK

Read this passage carefully.

# VISIT THE BIRDERIE

*. . . and spread your wings!*

The Birderie is Grainshire's most exciting family resort. Set in 25 acres of English countryside, The Birderie is home to hundreds of birds – the beautiful, the exotic, the shy, the sociable, the fierce, the friendly and the just plain weird!

5     Get eyeball to eyeball with diving penguins in our Underwater Walk. Trail through the treetops on our Bird's Eye View tour and watch the hawks catch their prey mid-flight in our Falconry Fiesta. Sneak a peek at the shamelessly flirtatious lovebirds in our African Aviary and munch
10 your lunch with our chatty mynah birds.

    Visit Haystack Farm and witness chicks hatching out of their shells. Meet Chanticleer the famous cockerel and his many wives. Paddle your own canoe around Donald's Duckpond and watch feeding time for our fabulous
15 flamingos and crowned cranes on the Tropical Lake.

    The Birderie is home to exciting birds from all over the world, but it has a serious side too. Avian Hospital cares for sick and injured birds brought in from all over the UK. Our scientists and conservationists carry out essential work
20 in learning how to preserve endangered species, safeguard threatened habitats, monitor our own bird population and analyse the effects of invasive species, farming practices and diminishing nesting areas. You can see our experts at work and watch, in our comfortable cinema, the fascinating
25 and moving film 'Flying to Live'.

    Why not take part in our Bird Identity Parade and learn how to identify the birds around us? You'll be amazed to learn how many birds you can see in your own neighbourhood. Find out how you can contribute to looking
30 after the birds in your own garden or local park.

    Come out of your shell and spread your wings! Visit The Birderie for a cracking day out!

Now read these questions. You have a choice of four answers to each question. Choose the *one* answer you think the best. Draw a line in the box next to its letter, like this.

A ▭

**61** How many adjectives can you find in paragraph 1?

  **A** nine
  **B** seven
  **C** five
  **D** ten

61   2

**62** An 'acre', line 2, is a measurement of space. Three of the words listed below are also measurements of space or distance. Which one is *not*?

  **A** hectare
  **B** knot
  **C** square mile
  **D** league

62   2

**63** The first paragraph explains that there are many different birds in The Birderie. Which of the words below would best complete the sentence?

    The collection of birds in The Birderie is remarkable for its _____.

  **A** colour
  **B** diversity
  **C** strangeness
  **D** behaviour

63   2

MARK ▭

## Comprehension

MARK

**64** What is the main point of the second paragraph?

   A  to describe the variety of things that visitors can do at the Birderie

   B  to show the cleverness of the birds

   C  to list the different levels of bird life at the Birderie

   D  to let visitors know how closely they can get involved with the birds

A ☐ B ☐ C ☐ D ☐     **64** ☐ 2

**65** The phrases 'Underwater Walk', 'trail through the treetops', 'Falconry Fiesta', 'sneak a peek', 'African Aviary' and 'munch your lunch' appear in the second paragraph. Which *two* of the following best describe the writing techniques used?

      1. rhyme  2. imagination  3. description  4. alliteration

   A  2 and 3

   B  2 and 1

   C  4 and 1

   D  4 and 3

A ☐ B ☐ C ☐ D ☐     **65** ☐ 2

**66** A 'Tropical Lake' is mentioned (line 15). Where would you normally find tropical places?

   A  north of the equator

   B  south of the equator

   C  north and south of the equator

   D  on the equator

A ☐ B ☐ C ☐ D ☐     **66** ☐ 2

**67** The words 'aviary' (line 9) and 'avian' (line 17) are derived from the Latin for the word 'bird', which is 'avis'. Which of the following has the same derivation?

   A  avoid

   B  aviator

   C  avocado

   D  avid

A ☐ B ☐ C ☐ D ☐     **67** ☐ 2

**68** Line 21 refers to 'threatened habitats'. Which of the following phrases means the same thing?

   A  frightening behaviour

   B  strange customs

   C  damaged homes

   D  endangered living areas

A ☐ B ☐ C ☐ D ☐     **68** ☐ 2

MARK ☐

## Comprehension

MARK

**69** Which of the words below would best complete the sentence?

Some of our species of birds are finding it hard to survive because areas of land in which they can nest are _____.

A invasive

B shrinking

C flooded

D dangerous

A ☐
B ☐
C ☐
D ☐

**69** ☐ 2

**70** What is the name that we give to a scientific expert on the subject of birds?

A an ornithologist

B an aviatrix

C a birdiologist

D a biologist

A ☐
B ☐
C ☐
D ☐

**70** ☐ 2

**71** What is the principal purpose of this article?

A to persuade people to visit The Birderie

B to educate people about birds

C to let people know what happens at The Birderie

D to explain the many different things birds do

A ☐
B ☐
C ☐
D ☐

**71** ☐ 2

Find the word that is used wrongly. Underline it and write the box letter at the end of the line.

**72** Theme parks are    under pressure to    provide more    felicities for visitors.

      A            B            C            D ☐

**72** ☐ 2

**73** Zoos employ    conversationalists to    study the health    of their inhabitants.

      A            B            C            D ☐

**73** ☐ 2

**74** Some species only    breed successively if    carefully nurtured    in captivity.

      A            B            C            D ☐

**74** ☐ 2

**75** One extraordinary    respect of birds is    their diversity in    appearance and size.

      A            B            C            D ☐

**75** ☐ 2

MARK ☐

COMPREHENSION SUB-TOTAL ☐ 30

## Q. 76–85 Short writing task

MARK

Write for 15–30 minutes on *one* of the following. Continue on a separate sheet if you need to.

a) The Visit

b) You are a bird perched on top of a tree near your home. Describe the scene in detail from your point of view.

c) Think of a theme park, animal centre, museum or other place to visit that you know well. Write a leaflet to advertise its attractions to potential visitors.

_____

_____

_____

_____

_____

_____

_____

_____

_____

_____

_____

_____

_____

_____

_____

_____

_____

_____

_____

_____

_____

END OF TEST

SHORT WRITING TASK SUB-TOTAL [     ] 10

English skills sub-total (from page 37) [     ] 60

Comprehension sub-total (from page 40) [     ] 30

Short writing task sub-total (from this page) [     ] 10

PROGRESS PAPER 5 TOTAL MARK [     ] 100

START HERE

## Q. 1–60 English skills

MARK

---

**Q. 1–5**

punctuation

Rewrite the sentence correctly, adding the necessary punctuation.

my favourite book said lily is horrid henry by francesca simon

_____

_____

_____

1–5 ☐ 5

---

**Q. 6–10**

direct
to indirect
speech

Change the text from direct to indirect (reported) speech.

**6** "Prepare to cast off!" the Captain ordered William.

_____

6 ☐ 1

**7** "Are you going to take the test?" asked Meena.

_____

7 ☐ 1

**8** "Be careful," said the plasterer to Dad, "the floor is unsafe."

_____

_____

8 ☐ 1

**9** "You're late again," the teacher told Sam as he slunk in.

_____

_____

9 ☐ 1

**10** "May I have some more?" asked Oli. "I'm still hungry."

_____

_____

10 ☐ 1

---

**Q. 11–15**

spelling

Fill in **ie** or **ei** to make the word.

**11** counterf ___ ___ t

11 ☐ 1

**12** sover ___ ___ gn

12 ☐ 1

**13** perc ___ ___ ve

13 ☐ 1

**14** n ___ ___ ce

14 ☐ 1

**15** w ___ ___ r

15 ☐ 1

---

MARK ☐

English skills

MARK

**Q. 16–20**

grammar

Write out the sentence, correcting any errors.

**16** She didn't speak very clear.

_____

16 ☐ 1

**17** The teacher learned him many facts.

_____

17 ☐ 1

**18** Me and her went shopping.

_____

18 ☐ 1

**19** He was so helpful, I could of hugged him.

_____

19 ☐ 1

**20** Priya lay the table before the meal.

_____

20 ☐ 1

**Q. 21–25**

similes

Put the word in the simile to which it belongs.

feather, sheet, mustard, die, eel

**21** as slippery as an    _____

21 ☐ 1

**22** as straight as a    _____

22 ☐ 1

**23** as white as a    _____

23 ☐ 1

**24** as keen as    _____

24 ☐ 1

**25** as light as a    _____

25 ☐ 1

**Q. 26–30**

spelling

Fill in **ie** or **ei** to make the word.

**26** inv ___ ___ gle

26 ☐ 1

**27** s ___ ___ ze

27 ☐ 1

**28** h ___ ___ fer

28 ☐ 1

**29** rec ___ ___ pt

29 ☐ 1

**30** s ___ ___ ve

30 ☐ 1

MARK ☐

English skills

MARK

| | | | |
|---|---|---|---|
| **Q. 31–35** | Write the missing parts of speech of the words shown in capitals. | | |

parts of speech, nouns, adjectives, adverbs

| | | NOUN | ADJECTIVE | ADVERB | |
|---|---|---|---|---|---|
| | Example: | BRAVERY | *brave* | *bravely* | |
| **31** | | LAZINESS | _____ | _____ | **31** ☐ 1 |
| **32** | | THOUGHT | _____ | _____ | **32** ☐ 1 |
| **33** | | DEPTH | _____ | _____ | **33** ☐ 1 |
| **34** | | HEIGHT | _____ | _____ | **34** ☐ 1 |
| **35** | | STRENGTH | _____ | _____ | **35** ☐ 1 |

**Q. 36–40**

abbreviations

Write the words that the abbreviation (shortened form) stands for.

**36** GB _____  **36** ☐ 1

**37** km _____  **37** ☐ 1

**38** USA _____  **38** ☐ 1

**39** app _____  **39** ☐ 1

**40** MP _____  **40** ☐ 1

**Q. 41–45**

spelling

Write out the sentence, correcting any misspellings.

**41** I was so suprised at my succes in the race.

_____  **41** ☐ 1

**42** I was jelous when he was made cheif monitor.

_____  **42** ☐ 1

**43** I would definately like to meet the auther.

_____  **43** ☐ 1

**44** The bilder was embarased when the cieling fell in.

_____  **44** ☐ 1

**45** I will start my own bisness if I get the oportunity.

_____  **45** ☐ 1

MARK ☐

## English skills

MARK

**Q. 46–50**

word meanings

Three words or phrases appear in brackets. Underline the *one* word or phrase that completes the sentence correctly.

**46** A vertebrate is a creature . . .
(with a spine, with a thick skin, able to swim and walk).

46 ☐ 1

**47** Something cumbersome is . . .
(loud and noisy, awkward and difficult to handle, cuddly and soft).

47 ☐ 1

**48** An ambidextrous person can do things . . .
(with both hands, with their eyes shut, incredibly fast).

48 ☐ 1

**49** Someone who gets out alive from a disaster is a . . .
(successor, submariner, survivor).

49 ☐ 1

**50** A carnivore is a person or animal who . . .
(enjoys parties, is good at games, eats meat).

50 ☐ 1

**Q. 51–55**

prepositions

Add the correct preposition to complete the sentence.

**51** He despaired _____ ever finding a job.

51 ☐ 1

**52** We protested _____ the army's use of force.

52 ☐ 1

**53** She was inspired _____ his teaching.

53 ☐ 1

**54** According _____ the website, the game is cancelled.

54 ☐ 1

**55** Can you comment _____ what you saw?

55 ☐ 1

**Q. 56–60**

join sentences

Join the two sentences *without* using *and, but* or *so*. Begin each new sentence with a word ending in *ing* and use a comma.
For example, *Ian left his warm bed. He shivered as he put on his slippers* becomes *Leaving his warm bed, Ian shivered as he put on his slippers.*

**56** Yossi spotted the burglar. Yossi raced after him.

_____

56 ☐ 1

**57** The dog picked up the bone. He buried it.

_____

57 ☐ 1

**58** I whistled my favourite song. I began vacuuming.

_____

58 ☐ 1

**59** He finished the race. He collapsed as he crossed the line.

_____

_____

59 ☐ 1

**60** Chloë hung on to the mugger. She shouted for help.

_____

60 ☐ 1

MARK ☐

ENGLISH SKILLS SUB-TOTAL ☐ 60

## Q. 61–75 Comprehension

MARK

Read this passage carefully.

### Holiday Heartbreak

*Laura and Rupa find themselves in a difficult situation.*

"It's only two weeks till we go!" enthused Laura.

"Oh, yeah. Hm!"

"I just can't wait to show you the White Water Rapids – it's just the most amazing fun in the whole resort!"

5 "I bet. Yeah! It must be."

"It's just brilliant that Mum and Dad said you could come. It'll be *so* much better than being on my own with Toby and Rajiv. They are *so* boring and they just want to play snooker the whole day."

"Er . . ." Rupa hesitated. "It *is* incredible that your mum and dad invited me. It was so kind of them. It's even more amazing that my parents said I could go . . . but . . ."

10 "Yeah! I didn't think they would either. I mean, they didn't even want you to come bowling when we went for Yasmin's party, did they?"

"No – well, they are a bit insane about homework, you know."

"I hope we're in the Lakeside Cabin – it's simply the best. You can watch herons flapping over the lake while you have breakfast. They have the most ginormous wings!"

15 "Hm! Sounds good. Er . . ."

"Er *what*? You're not sounding all that excited any more. You haven't gone off the idea?"

"Er . . ."

"Roops! What is it? What's happened?"

"Well, nothing exactly happened . . ."

20 "Well, then, *what*? You're my bestest friend!"

"I know! And you're mine! It's just . . ."

"*WHAT?*"

Rupa paused. She drew a deep breath.

"Imran's coming from America. He gets in the day we're supposed to be going away. He leaves the day

25 we get back. If I come away with you, I will miss him. *Completely!*"

Laura went very pale.

"Oh no. And I will miss him too!"

The girls stood still, in silence, both of them heartbroken, thinking of Rupa's film-star cousin and how, over all the years of their friendship, they had dreamed of meeting him.

Now read these questions. You have a choice of four answers to each question. Choose the *one* answer you think the best. Draw a line in the box next to its letter, like this.

A

**61** How many people are booked to go on the holiday?

A five

B four

C eight

D six

61  2

MARK ☐

## Comprehension

MARK

**62** Laura refers to the 'White Water Rapids' (line 3). What activity do you think takes place here?

A floating
B rafting
C rowing
D sailing

A ☐
B ☐
C ☐
D ☐

62 ☐ 2

**63** Rupa hesitates in line 8. Why?

A because she does not now want to go on the holiday
B because she has something to tell Laura and doesn't know how
C because she is worried about her parents
D because she doesn't want to be rude to Laura's parents

A ☐
B ☐
C ☐
D ☐

63 ☐ 2

**64** Which of the words below would best complete the sentence?

Rupa's parents are clearly very _____ about homework.

A demanding
B reasonable
C mad
D persistent

A ☐
B ☐
C ☐
D ☐

64 ☐ 2

**65** Laura enthuses about the 'most ginormous wings' of the herons (line 14). Which of the words below means 'to make something bigger'?

A expend
B expand
C export
D express

A ☐
B ☐
C ☐
D ☐

65 ☐ 2

**66** Which of the words below would best complete the sentence?

Rupa's revelation is likely to put a considerable strain on their _____.

A holiday
B conversation
C parents
D friendship

A ☐
B ☐
C ☐
D ☐

66 ☐ 2

**67** Which of the words below would best complete the sentence?

Unfortunately, Imran's visit exactly _____ with the holiday.

A concludes
B coincides
C coexists
D combines

A ☐
B ☐
C ☐
D ☐

67 ☐ 2

MARK ☐

## Comprehension

MARK

**68** Which of the words below would best complete the sentence?

The girls feel that to miss Imran's visit would be _____.

A incomparable

B imperceivable

C unimaginable

D unintentional

A ☐
B ☐
C ☐
D ☐

68 ☐ 2

**69** Why is '*Completely!*' (line 25) shown in italics?

A because it is a word on its own

B for emphasis

C because it has an exclamation mark

D because Rupa is upset

A ☐
B ☐
C ☐
D ☐

69 ☐ 2

**70** Identify the types of words contained in the phrase 'The girls stood still, in silence' (line 28).

A two nouns, one verb and an adjective

B one noun, one verb and an adjective

C two nouns, one verb and an adverb

D one noun, one verb and an adverb

A ☐
B ☐
C ☐
D ☐

70 ☐ 2

**71** Which term best describes the passage?

A dialogue

B monologue

C playscript

D discussion

A ☐
B ☐
C ☐
D ☐

71 ☐ 2

Find the spelling mistake. Underline it and write the box letter at the end of the line.

**72** Laura is likly to be | disappointed by | Rupa's news a | fortnight before their trip.

| A | B | C | D |

☐ 72 ☐ 2

**73** Rupa is having a | crisis of conscience | and has a difficult | descision to make.

| A | B | C | D |

☐ 73 ☐ 2

**74** Rupa's parents are | embarrassed as | Laura's parents have | payed a deposit

| A | B | C | D |

☐ 74 ☐ 2

**75** What actualy happens is that Imran can't come because of filming commitments.

| A | B | C | D |

☐ 75 ☐ 2

MARK ☐

COMPREHENSION SUB-TOTAL ☐ 3

48

Schofield & Sims • Progress Papers • English

## Q. 76–85 Short writing task

MARK

Write for 15–30 minutes on *one* of the following. Continue on a separate sheet if you need to.

a) Continue the story 'Holiday Heartbreak' from where it leaves off (page 46).

b) The Event

c) What makes a good friend?

SHORT WRITING TASK SUB-TOTAL [ ] 10

English skills sub-total (from page 45) [ ] 60

Comprehension sub-total (from page 48) [ ] 30

Short writing task sub-total (from this page) [ ] 10

PROGRESS PAPER 6 TOTAL MARK [ ] 100

# Short writing task tips

## Story writing

- Your story will work best if the action happens all in one go, in one location and with only a few characters.

- Don't write a long introduction. Plunge straight into the story – particularly if you are asked to continue the story from where it left off or to write from a particular character's viewpoint.

- Start with a small idea and develop it, rather than beginning with a huge idea for which you run out of time.

- Keep the story moving quickly to hold the reader's interest.

- Include dialogue and description that help the reader to imagine the events, setting and atmosphere.

## Concise description

- Think about the potential readers for your piece and write in a style that is likely to make them want to read on.

- For example, if the piece of writing is for a website or magazine, don't waste words – make it snappy and lively. You don't need detail for this type of writing. Make sure all you write is relevant to the task.

## Detailed description

- Where a full description is required, use your imagination to picture the scene.

- Use your senses – all of them! – to help your reader see and feel the scene as you do.

- Give the reader a strong sense of the person, place or thing that you are describing.

## Instructions, persuasive writing and explanations

Before you start writing, identify the purpose of the piece of writing.

- *Instructions* need to be simple, correctly ordered and straightforward. Sometimes the separate points may be numbered.

- *Writing that aims to persuade or to influence* should avoid nagging or insulting the reader. Carefully worked-out arguments – clearly expressed and with separate points that are in a helpful order – can be very effective.

- *Explanation* must be clearly focused on exactly what it is that the reader needs to understand. Be sure that you understand what you are trying to explain. You cannot provide a clear explanation of something that you do not understand.

## Discussion

- Show the reader that you understand the matter you are asked to discuss.

- Think clearly and express yourself as clearly and directly as you can.

- Strong opinions are not needed. Being able to see several sides to a question is a valuable skill.

- Simple sentences may work best in writing of this kind.

## Conversation and dialogue

- Some of the **Short writing task** options ask you to write a conversation, develop or create one or more characters, or speak in the voice of a particular character. We don't all speak the same way. Try to show this in the things you give your characters to say and in the different words you can find for the word *said*.

- All conversation should be correctly set out and punctuated.

# Topics chart

| English skills* | Paper | Book 1 | | | | | | Book 2 | | | | | | Book 3 | | | | | |
|---|---|---|---|---|---|---|---|---|---|---|---|---|---|---|---|---|---|---|---|
| | | 1 | 2 | 3 | 4 | 5 | 6 | 7 | 8 | 9 | 10 | 11 | 12 | 13 | 14 | 15 | 16 | 17 | 18 |
| **words** | abbreviations | • | | | | | | • | | | | • | | | | | | | |
| | alphabetical order | • | | | | | | | | | | • | | • | | | | | |
| | anagrams | | | | | • | | | | | | | | • | | | • | • | • |
| | antonyms | • | • | | • | • | | | • | • | • | | • | | • | • | | | • |
| | comparative and superlative | • | | | | | | | | | | | | | | | • | | |
| | homonyms | | • | • | • | • | | • | | • | | | | • | | | | • | |
| | homophones | | • | • | • | | | • | | • | | | | • | | | | | |
| | plurals | • | | | | | | | | | | | | | | | • | | |
| | prefixes | | • | • | | | • | • | | • | • | • | • | • | • | • | | | • |
| | spelling | • | • | • | | | | • | • | • | • | | • | | • | • | • | | • |
| | suffixes | | • | • | | | | • | • | • | | | | | • | • | | | • |
| | synonyms | • | | | | | • | • | • | • | • | • | | • | • | • | • | | • |
| **word choice and meaning** | odd one out (by meaning) | • | | • | | | | • | • | | • | | • | • | | | | | • |
| | word choice | • | • | • | • | | | • | • | • | • | | • | • | • | • | • | • | • |
| | word groups (by meaning) | • | • | • | | | | • | • | • | | | | | | | | • | |
| | word meanings | • | | | | | • | • | | • | | • | • | • | • | | • | • | • |
| **punctuation** | apostrophes for abbreviation | • | • | • | • | • | | • | | • | | | | • | | | | | • |
| | apostrophes for possession | • | • | • | • | • | | • | • | • | | | • | • | • | • | | | • |
| | punctuation | • | • | | | | | • | | • | | • | • | • | • | • | • | • | • |
| **grammar** | adjectives | | • | • | | | • | • | | • | | | • | • | • | • | • | • | • |
| | adverbs | | • | • | | | • | • | | • | • | • | • | | • | • | | | • |
| | grammar | | • | • | • | | • | | | | | • | | | • | | | | |
| | nouns | • | • | • | | | • | • | • | | • | | | • | | • | | • | • |
| | parts of speech | | | | | | | | | • | | • | | | | | • | • | • |
| | past tense | | | | | • | | • | | • | | • | | | | | | | |
| | prepositions | | • | | | • | | • | | • | | • | | | • | | | | |
| | verbs | | • | • | | • | • | • | • | | | • | | • | | • | | • | • |
| **write phrases** | popular phrases | | | | | | | • | • | • | • | • | | • | • | | • | • | • |
| | proverbs | | | | | • | | | | • | | • | | | | • | • | | • |
| | sayings | | | | | • | | | | • | | • | | | | | • | | |
| | similes | | | | | | | • | | | • | | • | | | | | • | |
| **write sentences** | direct to indirect speech | • | • | | | | • | | | | | • | | | | | | | |
| | indirect to direct speech | | | | | | | | | • | | | • | • | • | | | | |
| | join sentences | | | | • | | | | • | • | | | | | • | | | • | |
| | unscramble sentences | | | | | | | | | | | | | • | • | • | • | | |
| **Comprehension** | read and understand fiction | • | • | • | | | • | • | • | • | | • | | • | • | | • | • | |
| | read and understand non-fiction | | | | | | | | | | • | | • | | | • | | | |
| | read and understand persuasive texts | | | | | | | | | | | | | | | | | | • |
| | read and understand poetry | | | | | | | | | | | | | | | | | | • |
| **Short writing task** | write fiction | • | • | • | • | • | • | • | • | • | • | • | • | • | • | • | • | • | • |
| | write non-fiction | • | • | • | • | | • | • | • | • | • | • | • | • | • | • | • | • | • |

*Further work on English skills is included in the multiple-choice Comprehension questions throughout the series.

# Progress chart

Write the score (out of 100) for each paper in the box provided at the bottom of the graph. Then colour in the column above the box to the appropriate height to represent this score.

Score (out of 100)

| Paper 1 | Paper 2 | Paper 3 | Paper 4 | Paper 5 | Paper 6 |